750 Bed & Breakfasts

in Britain

For holidaymakers & business travellers

Overnight Stops & Short Breaks

Pubs & Inns

Wi-Fi Directory

2012

The Woodside, Southbourne, Dorset, page 63

York House, York, page 216

www.holidayguides.com

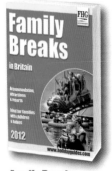

Contents

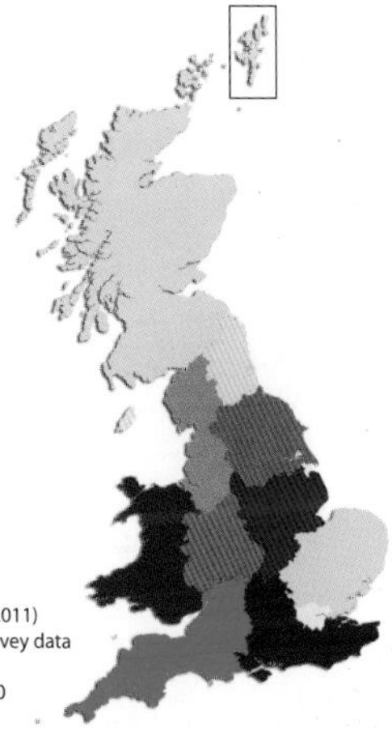

©MAPS IN MINUTES™ (2011)
Contains Ordnance Survey data
©Crown Copyright
and database right 2010

England and Wales • Counties

1. Plymouth	12. Windsor & Maidenhead	23. Milton Keynes	34. Blackpool
2. Torbay	13. Bracknell Forest	24. Peterborough	35. N.E. Lincolnshire
3. Poole	14. Wokingham	25. Leicester	36. North Lincolnshire
4. Bournemouth	15. Reading	26. Nottingham	37. Kingston-upon-Hull
5. Southampton	16. West Berkshire	27. Derby	38. York
6. Portsmouth	17. Swindon	28. Telford & Wrekin	39. Redcar & Cleveland
7. Brighton & Hove	18. Bath & Northeast Somerset	29. Stoke-on-Trent	40. Middlesborough
8. Medway	19. North Somerset	30. Warrington	41. Stockton-on-Tees
9. Thurrock	20. Bristol	31. Halton	42. Darlington
10. Southend	21. South Gloucestershire	32. Merseyside	43. Hartlepool
11. Slough	22. Luton	33. Blackburn with Darwen	

NORTH WALES
a. Denbighshire
b. Flintshire
c. Wrexham

SOUTH WALES
d. Swansea
e. Neath & Port Talbot
f. Bridgend
g. Rhondda Cynon Taff
h. Merthyr Tydfil
i. Vale of Glamorgan
j. Cardiff
k. Caerphilly
l. Blaenau Gwent
m. Torfaen
n. Newport
o. Monmouthshire

©MAPS IN MINUTES™ (2011) Contains Ordnance Survey data ©Crown Copyright and database right 2010

Boscastle

Cornwall

•Sunrise•

6 Burn View, Bude EX23 8BY
Tel: 01288 353214
sunriseguest@btconnect.com
www.sunrise-bude.co.uk

SB

Wi-Fi

Sunrise offers something special... with Four Stars and a Silver Award to prove it. Immaculate en suite accommodation providing comfort, style and service with a smile. Superb breakfasts and ideal location, opposite golf club, close to shops, restaurants and pubs. Ideal for short or long stays. Highly recommended. Ground floor room available.

Sunrise

Langaton Farm

Whitstone, Holsworthy
Devon EX22 6TS
Tel: 01288 341215

Margaret and Alan welcome you to holiday with them in their lovely stone-built 18th century farmhouse. It is surrounded by lawns and garden, centrally heated and tastefully decorated, to complement this charming 18th century home.

There are two guest bedrooms with en suite facilities, colour flat screen TV, hairdryer, towels, hospitality tray with fresh milk, and use of guest fridge.

After a busy day exploring the unique rugged North Cornish/Devon coast, relax in the garden room/conservatory overlooking the traditional stone farm buildings and garden.

Close to Boscastle, Tintagel, Clovelly, RHS Gardens Rosemoor; one hour by car to Eden Project.

Mrs Margaret Short • Bed and Breakfast from £28pppn, children under 12 half price. Weekly rate from £190.

e-mail: langatonfarm@hotmail.com
www.langaton-farm-holidays.co.uk

Hurdon Farm

SB

Launceston PL15 9LS
01566 772955
Mrs Margaret Smith

Wi-Fi

Elegant Listed 18th century farmhouse, idyllically tucked away amidst our 400-acre mixed working farm. Centrally positioned on the Cornwall/Devon border, it is ideally located for exploring the many attractions in both counties. Near the Eden Project. Six luxurious and spacious en suite bedrooms, all with TV, radio, tea/ coffee facilities and central heating. Comfortable guests' lounge. Superb English breakfasts and delicious four-course dinners, freshly prepared and cooked, are served at separate tables in the dining room.

Open May till November • B&B from £28
Free Wi-Fi access for guests

AA
★★★★
FARMHOUSE
HIGHLY COMMENDED

Colliford Tavern   "AN OASIS ON BODMIN MOOR"

SB

Colliford Lake, Near St Neot, Liskeard, Cornwall PL14 6PZ • Tel: 01208 821335
e-mail: info@colliford.com • www.colliford.com

Set in attractive grounds which include a children's play area, ponds and a working waterwheel, this delightfully furnished free house offers home cooked local food available 7 days a week. Sunday lunch also available. Sprucely-appointed guest rooms are spacious and have en suite shower, colour television, radio alarm, beverage maker and numerous thoughtful extras.

An unusual feature of the tavern is a 37' deep granite well. In the midst of the scenic splendour of Bodmin Moor, this is a relaxing country retreat only a few minutes' walk from Colliford Lake, so popular with fly fishermen. Both north and south coasts are within easy driving distance and terms are most reasonable.

enjoyEngland.com
★★★★
INN

Campsite for touring caravans, motorhomes and tents - full electric hook-up etc. available.

Liskeard, Lizard, Looe

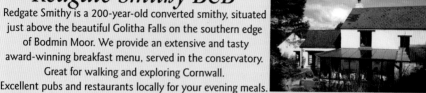

Renowned for its wonderful coastline, the longest in the UK, Cornwall has everything to offer for lovers of watersports, whether sailing, surfing, windsurfing, water-skiing, scuba diving or simply enjoying a family holiday on the beach. In busy fishing towns like Looe and Padstow, and traditional villages such as Polperro, there are plenty of inns and restaurants where you can sample the fresh catch. The best-known centre for the arts is St Ives, with the Tate St Ives, and artists and galleries are also to be found in Fowey, St Agnes and Penzance.

Mawgan Porth

SB

Wi-Fi

Blue Bay
HOTEL, RESTAURANT & LODGES

Trenance, Mawgan Porth,
Cornwall TR8 4DA
Tel: 01637 860324
e-mail: hotel@bluebaycornwall.co.uk
www.bluebaycornwall.co.uk

Blue Bay offers two different styles of
accommodation across two different sites,
beautifully situated in a tranquil location
between Padstow and Newquay,
overlooking Mawgan Porth beach.

Blue Bay Lodges
Five individually designed Cornish lodges, open all
year round. The lodges are located in the heart of
Mawgan Porth, overlooking the Vale of Lanherne
and beach. All fully equipped (sleep 4-8) with own
balcony or patio area. Linen, towels, electricity incl.
Laundry room. Dogs welcome.

Blue Bay Hotel
Located in Trenance on the cliff tops
overlooking Mawgan Porth beach, the hotel
has two garden rooms, two family suites,
one family room and one double room, all en
suite. Twin and single rooms available.

**Hotel prices
from £38pppn
Lodge prices from
£50 per Lodge per night.**

SB

BRE-PEN FARM

**Mawgan Porth
Cornwall
TR8 4AL**

A warm Cornish welcome awaits you from Rod and Jill in a friendly farmhouse on a working farm. The National Trust Coastal Path skirts the farm, making it an ideal walking area. The beaches of Mawgan Porth and Watergate Bay are within easy walking distance, both ideal for surfing. A short drive east takes you to the historic fishing port of Padstow, Bedruthan Steps and many glorious sandy beaches. Ideally situated for visiting the many attractions of Cornwall.

Double/Twin en suite rooms £32.50 pppn, Family suite £97.50. All with tea/coffee facilities and colour TV. Traditional farmhouse breakfast; vegetarians catered for. Holistic therapies available: Reflexology, Massage and Indian Head Massage. Free WiFi.

**Rod & Jill Brake, Bre-Pen Farm,
Mawgan Porth, Newquay TR8 4AL
Tel: 01637 860420 • www.bre-penfarm.co.uk
e-mail: jill.brake@virgin.net**

SB

Wi-Fi

Silver
SILVER AWARD

TREWITHEN FARMHOUSE is a renovated Cornish Roundhouse, set in a large garden and situated on a working farm enjoying country and coastal views. The picturesque town of Padstow with its pretty harbour and narrow streets with famous fish restaurants is only three miles away. St Merryn Parish boasts seven beautiful sandy beaches and bays. Also coastal walks, golf, fishing and horse riding on neighbouring farm. Hire a bike or walk along the Camel Trail cycle and footpath - winding for 18 miles along the River Camel. Eden Project 20 miles.

The accommodation has been tastefully decorated to complement the exposed beams and original features. All bedrooms are en suite with hairdryers, clocks, TVs and hot drink facilities.

*Mrs Sandra May,
Trewithen Farm, St Merryn,
Near Padstow PL28 8JZ
01841 520420 • 07709 635999
www.trewithenfarmhouse.com*

• *Parking* • *Full English breakfast* • *TV lounge.*
• *Bed and Breakfast from £40 per person per night.*
• *Winter breaks available.* • *Non-smoking.*

e-mail: maystrewithen@aol.com

SB

Bed & breakfast accommodation
in stunning West Cornwall

Lynn & Les Cox ⊡Bolankan Cottage

Crows-an-Wra, St Buryan, Penzance TR19 6HU
Tel: 01736 810168
Bolankancottage@talktalk.net
www.bolankan-cottage.co.uk

Fully modernised B&B approximately halfway between Penzance and Land's End. Double, twin and family rooms, all en suite with central heating, colour TV, hairdryer and tea/coffee making facilities.
Off-road parking.
*B&B from £60 per room
based on 2 sharing*

In summer, when the seaside towns are at their busiest, visit the Rame Peninsula in the south east of the county for a quieter break, or take a trip to the Isles of Scilly for a traditional and relaxing stay. Exotic gardens are a major attraction, whether long-established, like Trebah, Mount Edgcumbe and the Lost Gardens of Heligan, or the modern biomes of the Eden Project. The magnificent coast is ideal for birdwatchers, artists and photographers, golfers of every standard will find a wide choice of courses, while on Bodmin Moor, one of Cornwall's 12 Areas of Outstanding Natural Beauty, there is abundant evidence of a prehistoric past.

Polzeath

Seaways

Seaways is a small family-run guest house, 250 yards from a safe, sandy beach. Surfing, riding, sailing, tennis, squash, golf, and lovely cliff walks nearby. Polzeath is the ideal base for exploring all that North Cornwall has to offer. Padstow is a short distance by ferry; other places of interest include Tintagel, Boscastle and Port Isaac.

All bedrooms with en suite or private bathrooms - two double, one twin and a single room • Sittingroom; dining room • Children welcome (reduced price for under 10s) • Cot, high chair available. Comfortable family holiday assured with plenty of good home cooking.

Also available: self-catering annexe, sleeps 4. For details see www.crwholidays.co.uk (Ref RK23)

**Non-smoking establishment.
Open all year round.
Bed and Breakfast £40pppn.**

**Mrs P. White, Seaways, Polzeath PL27 6SU
Tel: 01208 862382
e-mail: pauline@seaways99.freeserve.co.uk
www.seaways-polzeath.co.uk**

Trenderway Farm

SB

Pelynt, Polperro, Cornwall PL13 2LY

Wi-Fi

Built in the late 16th century, Grade 2 Listed Trenderway Farm is a working farm set in 200 acres of beautiful countryside bordering Heritage Coastline, near to Polperro and Looe. We offer couples a perfect Cornish haven in luxuriously indulgent twin or double en suite bedrooms. To ensure you enjoy your farm holiday in Cornwall, every room or suite at Trenderway Farm has been painstakingly created with luxury, spaciousness and elegance in mind. King-sized beds come as standard, with plenty of space to really relax and make yourself at home. Each room has been individually designed with great attention to detail, with a unique atmosphere and appeal.

Our award-winning breakfasts from local produce are cooked to order on our Aga and served alongside a buffet in the conservatory overlooking our lake meadows.

25 minutes from the Eden Project, Trenderway is an ideal base from which to explore Cornwall.

Tel: 01503 272214
stay@trenderwayfarm.com
www.trenderwayfarm.co.uk

LONG CROSS HOTEL & VICTORIAN GARDENS
TRELIGHTS, PORT ISAAC PL29 3TF

Lovely Victorian country house hotel with four acres of restored gardens set in a beautiful tranquil location. Sit and relax on the terrace with its wonderful panoramic sea views. Close to golf, sailing, fishing, windsurfing, coastal walks, cycle hire and sandy beaches. The hotel has 14 refurbished elegant bedrooms all with private bathrooms, central heating, flat screen TVs, tea/coffee making facilities and broadband access. Many of the rooms have panoramic views. We are able to cater for those who are less mobile, with 3 rooms on the ground floor.

Tel: 01208 880243 • Fax: 01208 880560
e-mail: info@longcrosshotel.co.uk
www.longcrosshotel.co.uk

St Agnes

Ashburton

Devon

Think of Devon, and wild moorland springs to mind, but this is a county of contrasts, with the wild moors of the Exmoor National Park to the north fringed by dramatic cliffs and combes, golden beaches and picturesque harbours, and busy market towns and sleepy villages near the coast. An experience not to be missed is the cliff railway between the pretty little port of Lynmouth and its twin village of Lynton high on the cliff, with a backdrop of dramatic gorges or combes. In the centre of the county lies Dartmoor, with its vast open spaces, granite tors and spectacular moorland, rich in wildlife and ideal for walking, pony trekking and cycling. The Channel coast to the south, with its gentle climate and scenery, is an attractive destination at any time of year.

Lower Yelland Farm Guest House

Situated half way between Barnstaple and Bideford, this delightfully modernised 17thC farmhouse accommodation is part of a working farm. The farm is centrally located for easy access to the many attractions of North Devon, its beautiful beaches, varied walks and sports facilities including golf, surfing, fishing, riding etc. Its proximity to both Exmoor and Dartmoor makes this location perfect for those who wish to explore. Instow with its sandy beach, pubs and restaurants is a just mile away. It lies adjacent to the Tarka Trail, part of the South West Coastal Footpath, and RSPB bird sanctuary.

The bed and breakfast accommodation comprises 2 twin/super king-size and one room with four-poster bed, 2 double rooms and 2 single rooms; all rooms en suite, with TV and tea/coffee making facilities. Breakfast includes eggs from our free-range chickens, home-made bread, jams and marmalade. The delightful sitting room has a large selection of books for those who want to relax and browse.

FARMHOUSE ★★★★

Winner Golden
Achievement Award of
Excellence for Devon
Retreat of the Year

Please visit our website for further details
www.loweryellandfarm.co.uk

Lower Yelland Farm Guest House, Fremington, Barnstaple EX31 3EN
Tel: 01271 860101 • e-mail: peterday@loweryellandfarm.co.uk

Graham and Liz White, **Bulworthy Cottage**, Stony Cross,
Alverdiscott, Near Bideford EX39 4PY
Tel: 01271 858441

SB

Once three 17th century miner's cottages, Bulworthy has been sympathetically renovated to modern standards whilst retaining many original features. Our twin and double guest rooms both offer en suite accommodation, with central heating, colour TV, and many other extras. Relax in the garden with views across the countryside to Exmoor. Standing in quiet countryside, Bulworthy is within easy reach of the moors, Tarka Trail, South West Coastal Path, Rosemoor and numerous National Trust properties. We offer a choice of breakfasts and evening meals, using home grown and local produce. A selection of wines and beers to complement your evening meal is available.

B&B from £34pppn.

Silver AWARD

e-mail: bulworthy@aol.com • www.bulworthycottage.co.uk

GUEST ACCOMMODATION ★★★★

SB

West Titchberry Farm

Situated on the rugged North Devon coast, West Titchberry is a working traditionally-run stock farm, half a mile from Hartland Point.

The South West Coastal Path skirts around the farm making it an ideal base for walkers.

Pick ups and kit transfers available. Long term parking on site.

The three guest rooms comprise an en suite family room; one double and one twin room, with washbasins.

Bathroom/toilet and separate shower room on the same floor plus a downstairs toilet. All bedrooms have colour TV, radio, hairdryer, tea/coffee making facilities. Outside, guests may take advantage of a sheltered walled garden. Sorry, no pets.

Hartland village is 3 miles away, Clovelly 6 miles, Bideford and Westward Ho! 16 miles and Bude 18 miles.

- *B&B from £25–£30pppn (based on two sharing)*
- *3 Course Evening meal £15*
- *Children welcome at reduced rates for under 11s*
- *Open all year except Christmas*

Mrs Yvonne Heard, West Titchberry Farm, Hartland Point, Near Bideford EX39 6AU

Tel & Fax: 01237 441287

Riversford Hotel
and Riverview Restaurant

Limers Lane, Bideford, Devon EX39 2RG

The Riversford is a beautifully located hotel overlooking the River Torridge in peaceful North Devon. Enjoying fabulous, seasonal views all year round, the hotel offers warmth and friendliness to guests. Bideford is only a five minute drive away and The Riversford is ideally located for many attractions including Westward Ho!, Appledore, shopping centres, Arlington Court and Rosemoor Gardens.

There are fifteen en suite rooms, most overlooking the river. Four-poster rooms and suites also available.

The Riverview Restaurant (open to non-residents) opens every lunchtime and evening. We have an extensive à la carte menu and specialise in local seafood dishes. Cosy bar. Private car park.

Tel: 01237 474239
e-mail: Riversford@aol.com • www.Riversford.co.uk

Lake House Cottages and B&B

Lake Villa, Bradworthy, Devon EX22 7SQ
Brochure: Peter & Lesley Lewin on 01409 241962
e-mail: lesley@lakevilla.co.uk • www.lakevilla.co.uk

Peter and Lesley extend a warm welcome to B&B guests in their period home, with two extremely well appointed en suite bedrooms, a double and a twin. The rooms have tea/coffee making facilities and TV/DVD and share a sunny balcony overlooking the gardens. Situated on a private landing they are ideal for a family or friends holidaying together. Outside there are 1 acre of gardens, tennis, a 6 acre meadow, 2 lakes and coarse fishing.

Breakfasts (including vegetarian) use locally sourced, quality ingredients

Packed lunches available upon request. Dogs welcome by arrangement.

SELF-CATERING COTTAGES ALSO AVAILABLE

Brixham, Colyton

SB

Wi-Fi

SB

&

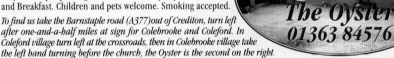

In the centre of the county lies Dartmoor, with its vast open spaces, granite tors and spectacular moorland, rich in wildlife and ideal for walking, pony trekking and cycling. The Channel coast to the south, with its gentle climate and scenery, is an attractive destination at any time of year. The long stretches of beautiful sandy beaches, pebble and shingle are intersected by river estuaries which provide shelter for migrating birds and other wildlife, and there are fascinating towns full of history to visit.

Dartmoor

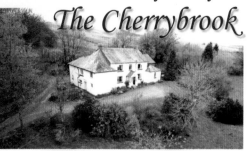

The Red Lion

has been offering generous hospitality since 1750 when it was a Coaching House. Log fires and gleaming brass in a friendly old bar, hearty English breakfasts, terraced gardens overlooking the River Dart, and an exceptionally warm welcome all await you.

Bedrooms are individually furnished, with comfortable beds, central heating, colour TV, tea-making facilities and telephones. An extensive menu includes daily specials and features fresh produce, prime local meats, fresh fish and locally grown vegetables. Picturesque countryside and a mild climate make this a perfect holiday retreat.

Mark and Judy Harrison welcome you to

THE
ROYAL
OAK INN
Dunsford, Devon

The Royal Oak is a traditional village pub with a friendly atmosphere, a large Beer Garden, and beautiful views across Dunsford and the Teign Valley. Quiet, newly refurbished en suite bedrooms are available in the tastefully converted 400 year old granite and cob barn located to the rear of the Inn. All non-smoking. Each room has its own front door which opens out onto a pretty, walled courtyard. Ideal base for touring Dartmoor, Exeter and the coast. Great for children, with our own play area and lots of animals. Dogs on leads are welcome. Plenty of off-road parking.

Exeter

symbols 🐎 SB & ♀ Wi-Fi

🐕	Pets Welcome		🐎	Children Welcome
SB	Short Breaks		♿	Suitable for Disabled Guests
♀	Licensed		Wi-Fi	Wi-Fi available

DEVONCOURT
—— H O T E L ——

Standing in four acres of mature subtropical gardens, overlooking two miles of sandy beach, yet within easy reach of Dartmoor and Exeter, Devoncourt provides an ideal base for a family holiday.

BEDROOMS: The accommodation is in 54 single, double or family rooms, all with private bathroom, colour TV, tea and coffee making facilities and telephone.

LEISURE: Swimming pool, sauna, steam room, whirlpool spa, solarium and fitness centre, snooker room, hair and beauty salon. For those who prefer to be out of doors there is a tennis court, croquet lawn, attractive outdoor heated pool, 18 hole putting green and golf practice area, all within the grounds. Free Wi-Fi throughout.

DINING: Brasserie 16 operate the attractive lounge bar and restaurant overlooking the fabulous gardens, with fantastic sea views from the large picture windows. Children's menus and vegetarian options available.

DEVONCOURT HOTEL
Douglas Avenue, Exmouth,
Devon EX8 2EX
Tel: 01395 272277
Fax: 01395 269315
e-mail: enquiries@devoncourt.com
www.devoncourthotel.com

Lynton/Lynmouth

SB

Wi-Fi

The North Cliff Hotel, standing in its own grounds, has some of the finest views of the North Devon coastline. It is in a peaceful position some 500 feet above sea level overlooking Lynmouth Bay, and a 200 metre walk to Lynton. With car parking facilities on the forecourt, the hotel is an ideal base for exploring the coastline and Exmoor National Park, whether it is your annual holiday or off-season break.

The rooms boast some of the best sea views in Lynton; bedrooms are individually decorated and are en suite. All bedrooms have colour television and facilities for making your favourite beverage.

We can accommodate family gatherings or walking parties as there are 7 doubles, 2 twins, 1 single and 4 family rooms (which can be used as twins or doubles).

We have a licensed bar available for a drink after a hard day of walking or an aperitif before dinner in our restaurant, which has magnificent sea and coastal views.

Children of all ages and pets are very welcome.

Local activities include walking, riding, tennis, and putting. The famous water-powered Cliff Railway linking Lynton and Lynmouth passes within a few feet of the hotel and is accessed via the stepped garden.

North Cliff Hotel
North Walk, Lynton, North Devon EX35 6HJ

Tel: 01598 752357
e-mail: holidays@northcliffhotel.co.uk
www.northcliffhotel.co.uk

Blue Ball Inn
formerly The Exmoor Sandpiper Inn

is a romantic Coaching Inn dating in part back to the 13th century, with low ceilings, blackened beams, stone fireplaces and a timeless atmosphere of unspoilt old world charm. Offering visitors great food and drink, a warm welcome and a high standard of accommodation.

The inn is set in an imposing position on a hilltop on Exmoor in North Devon, a few hundred yards from the sea, and high above the twin villages of Lynmouth and Lynton, in an area of oustanding beauty.
The spectacular scenery and endless views attract visitors and hikers from all over the world.

We have 16 en suite bedrooms, comfortable sofas in the bar and lounge areas, and five fireplaces, including a 13th century inglenook. Our extensive menus include local produce wherever possible, such as locally reared meat, amd locally caught game and fish, like Lynmouth Bay lobster; specials are featured daily. We also have a great choice of good wines, available by the bottle or the glass, and a selection of locally brewed beers, some produced specially for us.

Stay with us to relax, or to follow one of the seven circular walks through stunning countryside that start from the Inn. Horse riding for experienced riders or complete novices can be arranged. Plenty of parking. Dogs (no charge), children and walkers are very welcome!

Blue Ball Inn formerly The Exmoor Sandpiper Inn
Countisbury, Lynmouth, Devon EX35 6NE
01598 741263
www.BlueBallinn.com • www.exmoorsandpiper.com

SB

Woody Bay, Parracombe
Devon EX31 4RA
01598 763224

Moorlands, formerly the Woody Bay Station Hotel, is a family-run Guesthouse in a most beautiful part of North Devon, surrounded by Exmoor countryside and within two miles of the spectacular coastline.

Very comfortable and quiet single, double or family suite accommodation, all en suite with bath or shower, colour TV with DVD and beverage making facilities.

Moorlands has a licensed dining room and residents' lounge with open fire, all set in six acres of gardens. A perfect retreat for the country lover to relax and unwind.

Bed and Breakfast £33 - £39.50pppn.
Evening meals by arrangement from £16.
Some ground floor rooms and
self-catering apartments available.
Please see our website for special offers.

www.moorlandshotel.co.uk

Great Sloncombe Farm
Moretonhampstead Devon TQ13 8QF
Tel: 01647 440595

Share the magic of Dartmoor all year round while staying in our lovely 13th century farmhouse full of interesting historical features. A working mixed farm set amongst peaceful meadows and woodland abundant in wild flowers and animals, including badgers, foxes, deer and buzzards. A welcoming and informal place to relax and explore the moors and Devon countryside. Comfortable double and twin rooms with en suite facilities, TV, central heating and coffee/tea making facilities. Delicious Devonshire breakfasts with new baked bread.

Open all year~No smoking~Farm Stay UK
e-mail: hmerchant@sloncombe.freeserve.co.uk • www.greatsloncombefarm.co.uk

Paignton

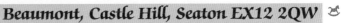

Sidmouth

symbols ⚘ 🎠 SB ♿ ♀ Wi-Fi

🐕	Pets Welcome	🎠	Children Welcome
SB	Short Breaks	♿	Suitable for Disabled Guests
♀	Licensed	Wi-Fi	Wi-Fi available

Berry Farm
Bed & Breakfast

SB

Wi-Fi

A warm and friendly atmosphere awaits you at this attractive Victorian farmhouse with views over glorious countryside and apple orchards. Situated in a small village 1.5 miles from historic Totnes, ideal for exploring the many places of interest in the area. Dartmoor 20 minutes' drive, beaches 10 minutes.

Tastefully decorated and colour co-ordinated bedrooms - one family, one twin and one double en suite, all with washbasins, tea/coffee facilities and TV. Bathroom with bath and separate shower. Guests' lounge and dining room; colour TV and video. Log fires. Delicious home cooking, vegetarian and special diets catered for.

**Berry Pomeroy, Totnes TQ9 6LG • Tel: 01803 863231
e-mail: geraldinenicholls@hotmail.co.uk
www.smoothhound.co.uk/hotels/berryfarm.html**

Sampford Manor

Bed & Breakfast on the edge of Dartmoor, near Tavistock

Double or Twin Bedded rooms with private bathroom or shower.
£30.00-£40.00 per person per night.
Dogs welcome.

Sampford Manor, Sampford Spiney, Yelverton, Devon PL20 6LH • Tel: 01822 853442
e-mail: manor@sampford-spiney.fsnet.co.uk • www.sampford-spiney.fsnet.co.uk

The FHG Directory of Website Addresses

on pages 390-400 is a useful quick reference guide for
holiday accommodation with e-mail and/or website details

Yelverton

Think of Devon, and wild moorland springs to mind, but this is a county of contrasts, with the wild moors of the Exmoor National Park to the north fringed by dramatic cliffs and combes, golden beaches and picturesque harbours, and busy market towns and sleepy villages near the coast. The award-winning resort of Woolacombe has everything to offer for a traditional family holiday, while Ilfracombe, originally a Victorian resort, provides all kinds of family entertainment including an annual Victorian festival. An experience not to be missed is the cliff railway between the pretty little port of Lynmouth and its twin village of Lynton high on the cliff, with a backdrop of dramatic gorges or combes. In the centre of the county lies Dartmoor, with its vast open spaces, granite tors and spectacular moorland, rich in wildlife and ideal for walking, pony trekking and cycling. The Channel coast to the south, with its gentle climate and scenery, is an attractive destination at any time of year. The long stretches of beautiful sandy beaches, pebble and shingle are intersected by river estuaries which provide shelter for migrating birds and other wildlife, and there are fascinating towns full of history to visit.

Dorset

Bournemouth

Bridport

SB

Wi-Fi

Wisteria Cottage
Morcombelake, West Dorset

Stunning panoramic views from our comfortable, well
equipped en suite guest rooms.
A friendly welcome and good food. Vegetarian and special
diets also catered for. VisitBritain Breakfast Award.
An ideal base for exploring the Jurassic World Heritage
Coast and historic towns of Lyme Regis and Bridport.
A walkers' paradise or just an idyllic spot for people
seeking tranquillity and fresh country air. Fossil hunting
equipment available for our guests' use.
Off road parking. Visit Britain Four Star Silver Award.
Open all year except Christmas and New Year.
Rooms from £65 - £75 per night for two persons sharing,
£45 – £55 single occupancy. Low season midweek breaks
also available. Call now for a brochure, or visit our website.

Contact Details:
Taylors Lane, Morcombelake, Dorset DT6 6ED
Tel: 01297 489019
www.dorsetcottage.org.uk
E-mail: dave@dorsetcottage.org.uk

SB

Wi-Fi

17th Century
FROGMORE FARM

Frogmore is a 90-acre grazing farm situated tranquilly in beautiful West Dorset,
overlooking the Jurassic Coast of Lyme Bay, and away from the crowds. Ideal for
walking or touring by car, our land is adjacent to National Trust land, to the cliffs and
coast (Seatown 1½ miles), and the South West Coastal Path.

One twin and two double bedrooms, all en suite, with TV and tea-
making facilities. Guests' dining room and cosy lounge with
woodburner. Not suitable for very young children or the infirm due
to very steep internal stairs and external steps.

Well behaved dogs very welcome • Open all year

• Car essential • Brochure and terms free on request

• Self-catering also available.

Contact Mrs Sue Norman • Tel: 01308 456159
Frogmore Farm, Chideock, Bridport DT6 6HT • www.frogmorefarm.com
e-mail: bookings@frogmorefarm.com

Dunster Farm

We invite you to relax and enjoy a carefree holiday in our 16th century farmhouse, situated in Broadoak, at the heart of the Marshwood Vale.

Our home has lots of character with traditional oak beams and a log fire. Dunster Farm is a real working farm, and children who visit are most welcome to help collect eggs and watch the milking of cows.
The heated bedrooms are all en suite, with radio clock alarm, TV and tea/coffee making. There is a lounge with TV. This is an ideal base for touring the South West, and the historic market town of Bridport is 4 miles away. The surrounding area offers activities such as horse riding , golf and fishing.

Dunster Farm, Broadoak, Bridport DT6 5NR
• Tel: 01308 424626 • Fax: 01308 423544
e-mail: dunsterfarm@onebillinternet.co.uk • www.dunsterfarm.co.uk

★★★ FARMHOUSE

SB

Britmead House

GUEST ACCOMMODATION

West Bay Road,
Bridport
Dorset DT6 4EG
Tel: 01308 422941
www.britmeadhouse.co.uk
e-mail: britmead@talk21.com

AA

★★★★ Guest Accommodation

SB

Wi-Fi

An elegant Edwardian house, family-run and ideally situated between Bridport and West Bay Harbour, with its beaches, golf course, Chesil Beach and Dorset Coastal Path.
We offer full en suite rooms (two ground floor), all with TV, tea/coffee making facilities, and hairdryer. South-facing lounge and dining room overlooking the garden.
Private parking •Non-smoking • Free Wi-Fi

SB

SB

Westwood House

29 High West Street, Dorchester DT1 1UP
01305 268018 • www.westwoodhouse.co.uk
reservations@westwoodhouse.co.uk

SB

Wi-Fi

Personally run by owners, Tom and Demelza Stevens, Westwood House offers comfortable, informal, non-smoking accommodation.
Each bedroom has digital TV, complimentary wi-fi, and tea/coffee making.
Breakfast is served in the light and airy conservatory.

A variety of pubs, restaurants and cafes are just a short stroll away.
The lovely market town of Dorchester has many places of historical interest, and is an ideal base for exploring the Dorset coast and countryside.

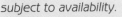

www.bandbdorchester.co.uk

Nicola and Gary Cutler would like to welcome you to their family run B&B within a few minutes' walk of the historic town of Dorchester.

Wi-Fi

They offer high quality accommodation in relaxed and luxurious surroundings. Bay Tree House is a late 19thC house that has been stylishly and imaginatively refurbished to a high standard. The rooms are spacious and light, and all rooms offer either en suite or private facilities. Double and twin bedded rooms are available; single occupancy subject to availability.

A five minute stroll along tree-lined pavements and avenues will take you straight to the heart of Dorchester's shopping centre, and a five minute stroll in the other direction will take you to Thomas Hardy's town house.

Athelstan Road, Dorchester DT1 1NR
Tel: 01305 263696
e-mail: info@baytreedorchester.com

Wi-Fi

Beech Farm • Sigwells

Bed & Breakfast in comfortable
farmhouse on 137-acre working
farm with beef and horses,
relaxed atmosphere.

A peaceful area on the Somerset/
Dorset border with wonderful
views from Corton Beacon.

*Four miles from the old abbey
town of Sherborne, six miles from Wincanton,
and just two miles off the A303.*

*B&B £25pppn • 10% reduction for two
or more nights; 20% for one week or more.*

*"Beacon" double bedroom with en suite
"Cleeve" twin bedroom
"Clouds" double attic bedroom
Guest bathroom*

All with TV and hospitality trays.
Pets and horses by arrangement.
Open all year except Christmas.

Mrs Susan Stretton
**Sigwells, Charlton Horethorne,
Near Sherborne, Dorset DT9 4LN
Tel: 01963 220524
e-mail: beechfarm@sigwells.co.uk
www.sigwells.co.uk**

In Dorset on the south coast, there are resorts to suit everyone, from traditional, busy Bournemouth with 10 kilometres of sandy beach and a wide choice of entertainment, shopping and dining, to the quieter seaside towns of Seatown, Mudeford and Barton-on-Sea, and Charmouth with its shingle beach. Lulworth Cove is one of several picturesque little harbours. In 2012 attention will be focussed on Weymouth, the venue for the Olympic and Paralympic sailing events, and one of several very popular sailing centres along the coast. Fossil hunters of all age groups are attracted by the spectacular cliffs of the Jurassic Coast, a World Heritage Site, and walkers can enjoy the wonderful views from the South West Coast Path at the top. With almost half the county included in Areas of Outstanding Natural Beauty, walking enthusiasts have downs, heathland, woodlands and river valleys, country villages and market towns to explore, even into the New Forest, with all it has to offer.

Please note...

Gloucestershire

A warm and friendly welcome awaits you at our completely refurbished
15th century Grade ll Listed farmhouse, in the heart of this beautiful village.

Spacious beamed rooms, inglenook fireplace in dining room where a full
English breakfast is served. Large private car park at rear.
All bedrooms are en suite and have coffee/tea making facilities, TV, radio and hairdryer.

SB

Wi-Fi

Accommodation comprises two double, two twin and one family suite
consisting of a single and a double room en suite.

Sorry no pets allowed in the house.

Non-smoking. No children under 12.

*Terms per night: from £65 per suite, 2 persons sharing.
More than two nights from £60. Family room for 3 persons sharing £90.*

Veronica Stanley,
Home Farm House,
Ebrington, Chipping Campden
GL55 6NL
Tel & Fax: 01386 593309
willstanley@farmersweekly.net
www.homefarminthecotswolds.co.uk

Holly House **AA**
Bed & Breakfast

Ideally situated for touring the Cotswolds and
Shakespeare's country. Double, twin and family rooms
available, all beautifully appointed with en suite facilities.
TV and tea and coffee. Private parking. Lovely garden
room at guests' disposal. Village pub serves meals.
Bike hire available locally.

Double room £65-£75 • Single room £55-£60 • Family room £80-£95 • Child reductions
Ebrington, Chipping Campden GL55 6NL   01386 593213
e-mail: info.hollyhouse@btinternet.com • www.hollyhousebandb.co.uk

Just to the north of Bath, Gloucestershire forms the major part of the Cotswolds Area of Outstanding Natural Beauty, with gently rolling hills, sleepy villages and market towns full of character and wonderful local food to sample, altogether ideal for a relaxing break whatever the season. There are gardens to visit, country pubs, antiques, craft and farm shops, cathedrals and castles, as well as all kinds of outdoor activities, from horse riding and 4x4 off-road driving to all the watersports on offer at the Cotswold Water Park, in the south east corner of the county. Canoeing, kayaking, climbing and abseiling are all available in the Wye Valley, while the dedicated cycle routes in the Forest of Dean are ideal for families. There's a vast network of underground caves just waiting to be explored, or walk above ground on the local paths or long distance trails.

SB

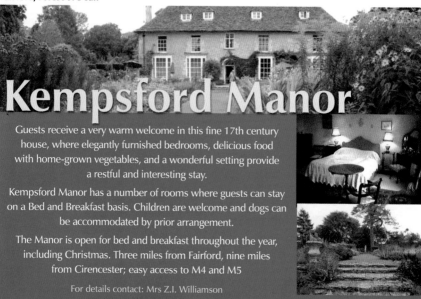

Kempsford Manor

Guests receive a very warm welcome in this fine 17th century house, where elegantly furnished bedrooms, delicious food with home-grown vegetables, and a wonderful setting provide a restful and interesting stay.

Kempsford Manor has a number of rooms where guests can stay on a Bed and Breakfast basis. Children are welcome and dogs can be accommodated by prior arrangement.

The Manor is open for bed and breakfast throughout the year, including Christmas. Three miles from Fairford, nine miles from Cirencester; easy access to M4 and M5

For details contact: Mrs Z.I. Williamson

Near Fairford, Gloucestershire GL7 4EQ
Tel & Fax: 01285 810131 • e-mail: info@kempsfordmanor.com
www.kempsfordmanor.com

SB

Wi-Fi

Farmhouse B&B in The Royal Forest of Dean
www.drysladefarm.co.uk

AA

Daphne Gwilliam
DRYSLADE FARM
English Bicknor, Coleford,
Gloucs GL16 7PA
daphne@drysladefarm.co.uk
Tel: 01594 860259
Mobile: 07766 631988

Daphne and Phil warmly welcome you to this 18th century farmhouse on their family-run working farm • Situated in Royal Forest of Dean and close to Symonds Yat, ideal for walking, cycling and canoeing • Excellent traditional farmhouse breakfast using local produce served in conservatory overlooking gardens
• Cosy guest lounge • Well behaved dogs welcome
• All rooms in house non-smoking • Reductions for children.

SB

THE FOUNTAIN
★★★ INN
INN & LODGE

Parkend, Royal Forest of Dean, Gloucestershire GL15 4JD.

Traditional village inn, well known locally for its excellent meals and real ales. A Forest Fayre menu offers such delicious main courses as Lamb Shank with Redcurrant and Rosemary Sauce and locally made sausages, together with a large selection of curries, vegetarian dishes, and other daily specials.

Centrally situated in one of England's foremost wooded areas, the inn makes an ideal base for sightseeing, or for exploring some of the many peaceful forest walks nearby.

All bedrooms (including one specially adapted for the less able) are en suite, decorated and furnished to an excellent standard, and have television and tea/coffee making facilities.

Tel: 01594 562189 • Fax: 01594 564438 • e-mail: thefountaininn@aol.com • www.thefountaininnandlodge.com

South Hill
Farmhouse

Juliet and Graham Druce welcome you to South Hill Farmhouse. The house is a Listed Cotswold stone farmhouse (no longer a working farm) situated on the ancient Roman Fosse Way on the outskirts of Stow-on-the-Wold. There is ample parking for guests, and it is only 10 minutes' walk to the pubs, restaurants and shops of Stow-on-the-Wold.

Single £60, double/twin £75, family (three) £135, (four) £140 per room per night, including generous breakfast. Non-smoking house.

South Hill Farmhouse, Fosseway, Stow-on-the-Wold GL54 1JU
Tel: 01451 831888 • Fax: 01451 832255
e-mail: info@southhill.co.uk
www.southhill.co.uk

SB

Wi-Fi

Bed and Full English Breakfast from £25 (reductions for children)

AA ★★★ Farmhouse

A traditional farmhouse with spectacular views of Cotswold countryside. Quiet location one mile from Stow. Ideally situated for exploring all Cotswold villages including Bourton-on-the-Water, Broadway, Burford and Chipping Campden. Within easy reach of Cheltenham, Oxford and Stratford-upon-Avon; also places of interest such as Blenheim Palace, Warwick Castle and many National Trust houses and gardens. Family, twin and double bedrooms; mostly en suite. TV, tea tray and hairdryer in all rooms. Relaxing guest lounge/dining room with Free Wi-Fi. Excellent pub food five minutes' walk away. Children welcome. Open all year.

Robert Smith and Julie-Anne, Corsham Field Farmhouse, Bledington Road, Stow-on-the-Wold GL54 1JH • 01451 831750 • Fax: 01451 832247 e-mail: farmhouse@corshamfield.co.uk • www.corshamfield.co.uk

THE LIMES

Large Country House with attractive garden, overlooking fields. Four minutes to town centre. One four-poster bedroom; double, twin or family rooms, all en suite. Tea/coffee making facilities, colour TV in all rooms. TV lounge. Central heating. Children and pets welcome. Car park.

Bed and Full English Breakfast from £30 to £35pppn.
Open all year except Christmas. *Established over 30 years.*

Evesham Road, Stow-on-the-Wold GL54 1EN Tel: 01451 830034/831056
e-mail: gkeyte@sky.com
www.thelimescotswolds.co.uk

SB

THE ***Old Stocks***
Hotel, Restaurant & Bar
The Square,
Stow-on-the-Wold GL54 1AF

Ideal base for touring this beautiful area.
Tasteful guest rooms in keeping with
the hotel's old world character, yet with
modern amenities. 3-terraced patio garden with smoking area.

Mouth-watering menus offering a wide range of choices.

Special bargain breaks also available.

AA
★★
SMALL HOTEL

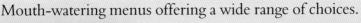

Tel: 01451 830666
Fax: 01451 870014
e-mail: fhg@oldstockshotel.co.uk
www.oldstockshotel.co.uk

SB

Wi-Fi

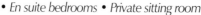

Orchardene

Castle Street, Kings Stanley,
Stonehouse, Gloucestershire GL10 3JX

A traditional Cotswold bed and breakfast where the welcome is always warm. One twin bedroom with an en suite bathroom and one double bedroom with private bathroom. Each room has tea/coffee facilities, toiletries and hairdryer. Free Wi-Fi. Ideal location to explore undiscovered Cotswolds and Severn Vale; glorious walks. Evening meal and packed lunches by arrangement. Local and organic food. Pets welcome.

01453 822684 • e-mail: info@orchardene.co.uk
www.orchardene.co.uk

Ireley is an 18th century farmhouse located in the heart of gentle countryside, one-and-a-half miles from Winchcombe and within easy reach of Cheltenham, Gloucester, Stratford-upon-Avon and Worcester.

Ireley Farm

The cosy yet spacious guest rooms (one double and two twin) offer either en suite or private bathroom. Relax in the evening beside a traditional open fire and in the morning enjoy a delicious English breakfast. Families are welcome, to enjoy the unique atmosphere of this working farm.

**Mrs Margaret Warmington, Ireley Farm,
Broadway Road, Winchcombe GL54 5PA
Tel: 01242 602445 • e-mail: warmingtonmaggot@aol.com**

B&B from £28.50 per person.

Ashbrittle, Bath

Somerset

SB

Bath

Bath

Marlborough House
1 Marlborough Lane, Bath BA1 2NQ
Tel: +44 (0)1225 318175 • Fax: +44 (0)1225 466127

Marlborough House is an enchanting, Victorian Guest House located at the edge of Royal Victoria Park, close to the heart of Georgian Bath and all the major attractions.

Each bedroom is handsomely furnished with antiques and contains either an antique wood four-poster, or a Victorian brass and iron bed. All are comfortable and scrupulously clean, with complimentary sherry and a hostess tray. Each has direct-dial telephone, wifi, alarm/radio, hairdryer, and colour TV.

AA

Served in either the elegant parlour or lovely dining room, breakfasts are cooked to order, using only the highest quality organic ingredients. Quote FHG

www.marlborough-house.net

WALTONS GUEST HOUSE
17 Crescent Gardens, Upper Bristol Road, Bath BA1 2NA
Tel: 01225 426528 • Fax: 01225 420350

SB

Wi-Fi

A warm welcome is assured in this gracious family-run Victorian home which offers an excellent base, minutes' walk from all the major attractions in the heart of Georgian Bath.

There are 10 double/ twin rooms, three single and two family rooms, five of which are en suite. Delicious full English Breakfast. Open all year. Group bookings catered for. Public car park at rear.

B&B £35-£50 single, £50-£85 double/twin, £50-£100 family room.

www.bathguesthouse.com • e-mail: rose@waltonsguesthouse.co.uk

AA

Wellsway Guest House
www.wellswayguesthouse.com

A comfortable Edwardian house with all bedrooms centrally heated; washbasin and colour television in the rooms. On bus route with buses to and from the city centre every few minutes or an eight minute walk down the hill. Alexandra Park, with magnificent views of the city, is five minutes' walk. ath is ideal for a short or long holiday with many attractions in and around the city; Longleat, Wells and Bristol are all nearby. Parking available.

Mrs D. Strong,
Wellsway Guest House,
51 Wellsway,
Bath BA2 4RS
01225 423434

Bed and Breakfast from £35 single, £60 double, with a pot of tea to welcome you on arrival

Leigh Farm
Bed & Breakfast and Self-Catering Accommodation

Leigh Farm is a working beef and sheep farm, situated at Pensford and close to Bath and Bristol. Bristol International Airport 10 miles approx.

Bed and Breakfast is offered in this 200 year-old comfy, warm farmhouse, with open log fire in the comfortable guest lounge in winter months. Central heating, TV. Accommodation comprises double en suite and family room with private bathroom; extra bedrooms in self-catering units when available, serviced on B&B basis. Access at all times.

Self Catering Accommodation available in four family bungalows and one bungalow suitable for couples. The open-plan bungalows are very sturdily constructed, with either one or two bedrooms, sleeping 2-4 persons. Regret no smoking, no pets.

**For brochure contact: Josephine Smart,
Leigh Farm, Pensford, Near Bristol BS39 4BA
Tel & Fax: 01761 490281 • www.leighfarmholidays.co.uk**

Brinsea Green Farm

Brinsea Green is a period farmhouse surrounded by open countryside. Set in 500 acres of farmland, it has easy access from the M5, (J21), A38 and Bristol Airport. Close to the Mendip Hills, the historic cities of Bath, Bristol and Wells, plus the wonders of Cheddar Gorge and Wookey Hole.

Wi-Fi

Comfortably furnished en suite/shower bedrooms offer lovely views, complimentary beverage tray, TV, hair dryer and Wi-Fi. Both lounge and dining room have inglenook fireplaces, log fires in winter.

SINGLE FROM £38.00   DOUBLE FROM £62.00

**Mrs Delia Edwards, Brinsea Green Farm
Brinsea Lane, Congresbury, Near Bristol BS49 5JN
Tel: Churchill (01934) 852278**

e-mail: delia@brinseagreenfarm.co.uk
www.brinseagreenfarm.co.uk

SB

North Down Farm

In tranquil, secluded surroundings on the Somerset/Devon Border. Traditional working farm set in 100 acres of natural beauty with panoramic views of over 40 miles, on the edge of Exmoor. M5 7 miles, Taunton 10 miles. All rooms tastefully furnished to high standard include en suite, TV, and tea/coffee facilities. Double, twin or single rooms available. Dining room and lounge with log fires for our guests' comfort; centrally heated and double glazed. Drying facilities. Delicious home produced food a speciality. Fishing, golf, horse riding and country sports nearby. Dogs welcome.

Bed and Breakfast from £38 pppn,
Seven nights B&B and Evening Meals £310pp.
North Down Break: three nights B&B and Evening Meals £160 per person.

Jenny Blackshaw, North Down Farm, Pyncombe Lane,
Wiveliscombe, Taunton TA4 2BL
Tel: 01984 623730 • Mob: 07729 846401
e-mail: jenniferblackshaw@btinternet.com • www.north-down-farm.co.uk

---

Other British holiday guides from FHG Guides

SHORT BREAK HOLIDAYS in Britain

The bestselling and original **PETS WELCOME!**

The GOLF GUIDE, Where to Play, Where to Stay in Britain & Ireland

800 GREAT PLACES TO STAY in Britain

SELF-CATERING HOLIDAYS in Britain

CARAVAN & CAMPING HOLIDAYS in Britain

FAMILY BREAKS in Britain

Published annually: available in all good bookshops or direct from the publisher:

FHG Guides, Abbey Mill Business Centre, Seedhill, Paisley PA1 1TJ

Tel: 0141 887 0428 • Fax: 0141 889 7204

e-mail: admin@fhguides.co.uk • www.holidayguides.com

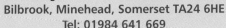

Somerset shares in the wild, heather-covered moorland of Exmoor, along with the Quantock Hills to the east, ideal for walking, mountain biking, horse riding, fishing and wildlife holidays. The forty miles of coastline with cliffs, sheltered bays and sandy beaches includes family resorts like Weston-super-Mare, with its famous donkey rides and brand new pier with 21st century facilities and entertainment for everyone. More family fun can be found at Minehead and Burnham-on-Sea, or opt for the quiet charm of Clevedon. With theatres, festivals, museums, galleries, gardens, sporting events and of course, shopping, the city of Bath has everything for a short break or longer stay. Attracting visitors from all over the world, this designated World Heritage Site boasts wonderful examples of Georgian architecture and of course, the Roman Baths.

Taunton

Wells

Wiltshire

Scotland Lodge Farm

Warm welcome at family-run competition yard set in 46 acres of grassland. Lovely views and walks. Stonehenge and Salisbury nearby. Three attractive, comfortable rooms - double with private bathroom; twin and double on ground floor. Conservatory and garden for guests' use. Dogs by arrangement. French, Italian and German spoken. Easy access off A303 with entry through automatic gate. Excellent local pubs.

**Scotland Lodge Farm,
Winterbourne Stoke
Salisbury SP3 4TF
Tel: 01980 621199**

Mobile: 07763 083585 • e-mail: catherine.lockwood@bigwig.net

www.scotlandlodgefarm.co.uk

Spinney Farmhouse ~ Thoulstone, Chapmanslade, Westbury BA13 4AQ

Off A36, three miles west of Warminster; 16 miles from historic city of Bath. Close to Longleat, Cheddar and Stourhead. Reasonable driving distance to Bristol, Stonehenge, Glastonbury and the cathedral cities of Wells and Salisbury. Discounts on Longleat tickets.

• Washbasins, tea/coffee-making facilities and shaver points in all rooms.
• Family room available. • Guests' lounge with colour TV.
• Central heating. • Children and pets welcome.
• Ample parking. • Open all year. • No smoking
Enjoy farm fresh food in a warm, friendly family atmosphere.
Bed and Breakfast from £26 per night. Reduction after 2 nights.
Evening Meal £12.
Telephone: 01373 832412 • e-mail: isabelandbob@btinternet.com

---

symbols 🐕🙂SB♿️♒Wi-Fi

🐕	*Pets Welcome*	🙂	*Children Welcome*
SB	*Short Breaks*	♿	*Suitable for Disabled Guests*
♒	*Licensed*	**Wi-Fi**	*Wi-Fi available*

Looking for Holiday Accommodation?
then visit our website:
www.holidayguides.com

**Search for holiday accommodation
by region, location, type of accommodation
(B&B, Self-Catering, Hotel etc)**

©MAPS IN MINUTES™ (2011)
Contains Ordnance Survey data
©Crown Copyright and database right 2010

**Special requirements –
Are you looking for accommodation
where children and pets are welcome,
or maybe you want to be
close to a golf course...**

for details of hundreds of properties throughout the UK

London (Central & Greater)

SB

Wi-Fi

SB

Queens Hotel

33 Anson Road, Tufnell Park, LONDON N7 0RB

Tel: 0207 607 4725 • Fax: 0207 697 9725

stay@queenshotellondon.co.uk • www.queenshotellondon.co.uk

The Queens Hotel is a large double-fronted Victorian building standing in its own grounds five minutes' walk from Tufnell Park Station. Quietly situated yet within easy reach of London Zoo, Camden, Hampstead, Highgate and Central London. Two miles from King's Cross and St Pancras Stations. Within walking distance of Arsenal Football Stadium. Many rooms en suite. Refurbished throughout in 2011.

All prices include full English Breakfast plus VAT.

Discounts on longer stays

We offer quality and convenience at affordable rates.
A VERY WARM WELCOME AWAITS YOU.

Single Rooms from £35-£55
Double/Twin Rooms from £45-£65
Triple & Family Rooms from £20 per person

All major credit cards accepted.

The Athena

110-114 SUSSEX GARDENS, HYDE PARK, LONDON W2 1UA

Tel: 0207 706 3866; Fax: 0207 262 6143

e-mail: stay@athenahotellondon.co.uk • www.athenahotel.co.uk

TREAT YOURSELVES TO A QUALITY HOTEL AT AFFORDABLE PRICES

The Athena is a newly completed family run hotel in a restored Victorian building. Professionally designed, including a lift to all floors and exquisitely decorated, we offer our clientele the ambience and warm hospitality necessary for a relaxing and enjoyable stay. Ideally located in a beautiful tree-lined avenue, extremely well-positioned for sightseeing London's famous sights and shops; Hyde Park, Madame Tussaud's, Oxford Street, Marble Arch, Knightsbridge, Buckingham Palace and many more are all within walking distance.

Travel connections to all over London are excellent, with Paddington and Lancaster Gate Stations, Heathrow Express, A2 Airbus and buses minutes away.
Our tastefully decorated bedrooms have en suite bath/shower rooms, satellite colour TV, bedside telephones, tea/coffee making facilities. Hairdryers, trouser press, laundry and ironing facilities available on request. Car parking available.

We offer quality and convenience at affordable rates.

A VERY WARM WELCOME AWAITS YOU.

Single Rooms from £50-£89
Double/Twin Rooms from £64-£99
Triple & Family Rooms from £25 per person
All prices include full English breakfast plus VAT.

All major credit cards accepted, but some charges may apply.

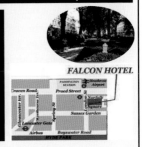
London has it all - theatres, shopping, concerts, museums, art galleries, pageantry and sporting events, a magnet for visitors from all over the world. In 2012, with the staging of the Olympic Games, the focus is on sport, but for visitors with other interests, there's plenty to see and do, from all the hands on activities of the Science Museum and the Natural History Museum, the National Gallery with one of the largest art collections in the world, the thought-provoking artworks at the Tate Modern, the splendour of Buckingham Palace and the magnificent gardens at Kew, to a sumptuous afternoon tea at a top hotel. With a wide range of accommodation at prices to suit every pocket, it's easy to spend a weekend here or a take a longer break.

Windsor

Berkshire

SB

Wi-Fi

- Town centre location.
- Licensed bar and steam room.
- High quality accommodation at guest house prices.
- All rooms have en suite bathrooms, TV, tea/coffee making facilities, radio alarms, hairdryers, free wi-fi and internet.
- Heathrow Airport 25 minutes by car.
- Convenient for Legoland and trains to London.

Clarence Hotel
9 Clarence Road, Windsor, Berkshire SL4 5AE
Tel: 01753 864436 • Fax: 01753 857060
e-mail: clarence.hotel@btconnect.com • www.clarence-hotel.co.uk

Just a short train ride away from central London, in Berkshire explore historic towns and villages, wander by the tranquil waters of the River Thames, visit gardens and great houses, like Basildon Park at Pangbourne. Windsor Castle is always major attraction, or have a fun day out at the races at nearby Ascot. Children will love Legoland, and the hands-on science at the Look Out Discovery Centre at Bracknell.

The FHG Directory of Website Addresses
on pages 390-400 is a useful quick reference guide for holiday accommodation with e-mail and/or website details

Aylesbury

Buckinghamshire

www.country-accom.co.uk/poletrees-farm

Poletrees Farm

SB

This working family farm provides spacious, comfortable 4 Star Bed & Breakfast ground floor accommodation for couples and individuals, whether on an overnight visit or longer.

- Non-smoking
- En suite bedrooms in 4 cottages with colour TV and tea/coffee tray

The Burnwode Jubilee Way cuts through the farm, and there are many places of historic interest in the area.

Ludgershall Road, Brill, Near Aylesbury, Bucks HP18 9TZ • Tel & Fax: 01844 238276

For deposits and bookings please phone or fax

e-mail: poletrees.farm@btinternet.com

AA
★★★★
Guest Accommodation

Only half an hour from London, the rolling hills and wooded valleys of the Buckinghamshire countryside provide a wonderful contrast to city life. Enjoy the bluebells in spring and the autumn colours of the woodland while following the innumerable footpaths, cycle paths, bridleways and two National Trails that cross the county and follow the meandering River Thames. Watch the red kites above the Chilterns, follow the Roald Dahl Trail or relax with a picnic in a country park. The excitement of the 2012 Olympics comes to Dorney Lake at Eton, for rowing, canoeing and kayaking events. Fascinating historic towns and villages include West Wycombe, owned by the National Trust, just one of many interesting properties in the area, while Milton Keynes is the destination for an all-round shopping experience.

DIFFERENT DRUMMER HOTEL

High Street, Stony Stratford, Milton Keynes, Bucks MK11 1AH
Tel: 01908 564733 • Fax: 01908 260646
info@hoteldifferentdrummer.co.uk
www.hoteldifferentdrummer.co.uk

Known as 'The Swan with Two Necks' until 1982, this historic coaching inn has been transformed into a superbly furnished hotel, while maintaining its olde worlde charm. Guest rooms are en suite, with colour TV and satellite channels, free Wi-Fi access, and tea/coffee making facilities.
The premises boasts an oak-panelled fine dining restaurant serving Italian and seafood dishes. There is also a modern and chic wine bar and restaurant, The Vine, which serves European and British fare, and an extensive selection of international wines.

★★★ SMALL HOTEL

Barton-on-Sea

Hampshire

Ideally situated for the delights of the New Forest, scenic cliff top walks, local beaches, pleasure cruises to the Isle of Wight, the Needles and historic Hurst Castle, horse riding, cycling, golf and a whole host of indoor and outdoor pursuits. Laurel Lodge is a comfortable, centrally heated, converted bungalow, offering twin, double and family rooms. All rooms are fully en suite with tea and coffee making facilities, comfortable chairs, colour TV and alarm clock radio. Ground floor rooms available. Breakfast is served in our conservatory/diningroom with views over the garden.

Lee & Melanie Snook, Laurel Lodge,
48 Western Avenue, Barton-on-Sea, New Milton BH25 7PZ
Tel: 01425 618309

Laurel Lodge

Bed and Breakfast from £30.00pp
Special deals for longer breaks
Children welcome, cot supplied by prior arrangement
Off-road parking for all rooms
Strictly no smoking
Open all year
Please phone for further details.

Idyllic countryside, sandy beaches, beautiful gardens and historic houses, country parks, museums and castles, and wildlife parks, are all there to enjoy in Hampshire. There are museums full of military heritage on land, sea and air, including the HMS Victory at Portsmouth, where a trip to the top of the Spinnaker Tower provides spectacular views of the surrounding area. Outdoors walk, cycle or ride on horseback over the heathland and through the ancient woodlands of the New Forest, and in the South Downs National Park, or try out one of the many watersports available along the coast. Boating enthusiasts will make for one of the many marinas, and the annual regatta on the River Hamble, and for courses on sailing, rockclimbing, and even skiing, where better to learn more than the Calshot Activities Centre on the shores of the Solent.

OAKLEA GUEST HOUSE

SB
Wi-Fi

**London Road,
Hook RG27 9LA
Tel: 01256 762673**
Please quote FHG

Friendly, family-run Guest House. All bedrooms en suite with TV and hospitality tray. Ample parking. Easy access from J5 M3, London 55 minutes by train.

Free wireless internet access available via own equipment.

GOLF: Many excellent courses within 10-mile radius.
HORSE RACING at Sandown, Ascot and Goodwood.
SHOPPING at The Oracle, Reading and Festival Place, Basingstoke.
DAYS OUT: Thorpe Park, Chessington, Legoland, Windsor Castle, Hampton Court, RHS Wisley, Milestones.

AA
★★★★
Guest House

e-mail: reception@oakleaguesthouse.co.uk • www.oakleaguesthouse.co.uk

---

Efford Cottage

SB

Everton, Lymington, Hampshire SO41 0JD

Tel: 01590 642315

Guests receive a warm and friendly welcome to our home, which is a spacious Georgian cottage. All rooms are en suite with many extra luxury facilities. We offer a four-course, multi-choice breakfast with homemade bread and preserves. Patricia is a qualified chef and uses our home-grown produce. An excellent centre for exploring both the New Forest and the South Coast, with sports facilities, fishing, bird watching and horse riding in the near vicinity. Private parking. Dogs welcome. Sorry, no children. Bed and Breakfast from £25–£35 pppn. Mrs Patricia J. Ellis.

AA
★★★★
Accommodation

Winner of "England For Excellence 2000"
FHG Diploma 1997/1999/2000/2003 / Michelin / Welcome Host
Awards Achieved: Gold Award / RAC Sparkling Diamond & Warm Welcome
Nominated Landlady of Year & Best Breakfast Award.
Enquiries and bookings by telephone only.

e-mail: pellis48@btinternet.com • www.effordcottage.co.uk

New Forest, Southampton

NEW FOREST. Mrs J. Pearce, "St Ursula", 30 Hobart Road, New Milton BH25 6EG (01425 613515).
Large detached family home offering every comfort in a friendly relaxed atmosphere. Off Old Milton Road, New Milton. Ideal base for visiting New Forest with its ponies and beautiful walks; Salisbury, Bournemouth easily accessible. Sea one mile. Leisure centre with swimming pool etc, town centre and mainline railway to London minutes away. Twin (en suite), double, family, single rooms, all with handbasin, TV and tea-making facilities. High standards maintained throughout; excellent beds. Two bathrooms/showers, four toilets. Cot etc, available. Pretty garden which guests are welcome to use. Two diningrooms. Smoke detectors installed. Full central heating.

Rates: Bed and Breakfast from £28.50.
• Downstairs twin bedroom suitable for disabled persons. • Children and pets welcome. • Open all year.
N.F.T.A. Quality Assessment *NATIONAL ACCESSIBLE SCHEME LEVEL 1.*

Bramble Hill Hotel
Bramshaw, New Forest, Hampshire SO43 7JG
Telephone: 023 80 813165
bramblehill@hotmail.co.uk • www.bramblehill.co.uk

Peacefully located in tranquil surroundings, this country house hotel is only three miles from Junction 1 of the M27 and is set in ancient woodland with 15 acres of glades, lawns and shrubbery to enjoy. Ideal for country walks and horse riding.

A short drive from many places of interest including Salisbury, Stonehenge, Winchester and Beaulieu.
All bedrooms have en suite bathrooms and some have antique four-poster beds.
A warm, friendly welcome and a hearty home-cooked breakfast assured.

Daily rates or weekly terms — please phone for details.

SB

Twin Oaks
GUEST HOUSE

SB

A warm welcome awaits in Twin Oaks Guest House in Hedge End town. Home-from-home comforts include modern en suite rooms with tea/coffee making facilities and television, and hearty breakfasts. Central heating. Car parking. No smoking.

Wi-Fi

Close to hotels/function centres, superstores and amenities, including county cricket ground (The Rose Bowl) and leisure centre. Situated near J7 of the M27 and therefore close to all routes to Portsmouth, Fareham, Winchester and Eastleigh. Also conveniently located close to Swanwick Marina and the Hamble Valley Country Park.

43 Upper Northam Road, Hedge End, Southampton SO30 4EA
Tel: 01489 690054 • Mobile: 07840 816052
e-mail: reservations@twinoaksguesthouse.co.uk
www.twinoaksguesthouse.co.uk

Isle of Wight

SB

The ultimate sailing destination is of course the Isle of Wight, only a short ferry ride away from the mainland, with marinas, golden, sandy beaches, water sports centres, seakayaking, diving, sailing and windsurfing. On land there are over 500 miles of interconnected footpaths, cycleways, historic castles, dinosaur museums, theme parks and activity centres, or view it all from the skies on a paragliding adventure. To the north and east the well-known resorts of Sandown, Shanklin, Ryde and Ventnor provide all the traditional seaside activities, as well as the sailing centre, Cowes, while West Wight, an Area of Outstanding Natural Beauty will appeal to nature lovers and birdwatchers. With a thriving arts community, and of course two internationally renowned music festivals held every year, there is something for everyone!.

Sandown, Totland

Ashford, Broadstairs

Kent

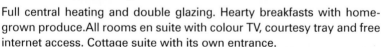

Dover, Folkestone

SB

Kent, the 'Garden of England', yet with such easy access to London, is a county of gentle, rolling downlands, edged by the famous White Cliffs and miles of sands and shingle beaches along the Channel coast. Walk along the North Downs Way through an Area of Outstanding Natural Beauty stretching from Kent through Sussex to Surrey, or enjoy the stunning scenery from the Saxon Shore Way with views to the coast of France, and the wildlife of the Medway Estuary and Romney Marsh. The resorts of the Isle of Thanet and the south-east coast, like Ramsgate, Margate, Herne Bay and Deal have plenty to offer for a traditional family seaside holiday, and there are steam trains, animal parks and castles full of history to explore too. At Leeds and Hever Castles visitors can even play a round of golf, just two of the wide choice of links, urban and countryside courses throughout the county.

Maidstone

SB
♀

Collina House

5 East Hill, Tenterden, Kent TN30 6RL
Tel: 01580 764852/764004 • Fax: 01580 762224
www.collinahousehotel.co.uk
e-mail: enquiries@collinahousehotel.co.uk

This charming house is quietly situated in the country town of Tenterden, yet is only a few minutes' walk from the Town Centre. There are many National Trust properties and places of interest in the area, including Sissinghurst Castle, Leeds Castle, Scotney Castle Gardens and the Kent and East Sussex steam engines. Personal attention is assured by the Swiss-trained owners who provide home cooking of the highest standard, enhanced by the use of home-grown produce. All the well-appointed bedrooms, including five family rooms, have private bathrooms, central heating, colour television, direct-dial telephones, tea-making facilities, and hairdryers. Further details on request.

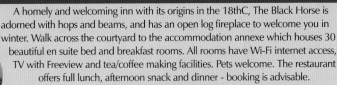

BLACK HORSE INN
Pilgrims Way, Thurnham, Maidstone ME14 3LD
Tel: 01622 737185 • info@wellieboot.net • www.wellieboot.net

🐎
🐕
SB
♀
♿
Wi-Fi

A homely and welcoming inn with its origins in the 18thC, The Black Horse is adorned with hops and beams, and has an open log fireplace to welcome you in winter. Walk across the courtyard to the accommodation annexe which houses 30 beautiful en suite bed and breakfast rooms. All rooms have Wi-Fi internet access, TV with Freeview and tea/coffee making facilities. Pets welcome. The restaurant offers full lunch, afternoon snack and dinner - booking is advisable.

An ideal base for a short walking or cycling break.There is a host of pathways, walkways and bridle paths from which you can enjoy spectacular countryside.

symbols 🐕🐎SB♿♀Wi-Fi

🐕	Pets Welcome	🐎	Children Welcome
SB	Short Breaks	♿	Suitable for Disabled Guests
♀	Licensed	Wi-Fi	Wi-Fi available

Oxfordshire

Oxfordshire, with the lively, historic university city of Oxford, the 'city of dreaming spires', at its centre, is ideal for a relaxing break. Quiet countryside is dotted with picturesque villages and busy market towns, while the open downland to the south is covered by a network of footpaths connecting up with the ancient Ridgeway Trail and the riverside walks of the Thames Path. Hire a rowing boat or a punt for a leisurely afternoon on the River Thames or explore the Cotswold villages to the west. Stretching from Oxford to the Cotswolds, the mysterious Vale of the White Horse is named after the oldest chalk figure in Britain, dating back over 3000 years. The historic market towns like Abingdon and Wantage make good shopping destinations, and all the family will enjoy the history, activities and beautiful gardens at Blenheim Palace.

THE OLD BAKERY

Skirmett
Near Henley-on-Thames
Oxfordshire RG9 6TD

This welcoming family house is situated on the site of an old bakery, seven miles from Henley-on-Thames and Marlow; half-an-hour from Heathrow and Oxford; one hour from London. It is in the beautiful Hambleden Valley in the Chilterns, with many excellent pubs. Village pub in Skirmett, within easy walking distance, serves superb food in the restaurant.

One double en suite, one twin-bedded room and one double with use of own bathroom, all with TV and tea making facilities.

Open all year. Parking for six cars (car essential). Children and pets welcome. Outstandingly beautiful garden/vegetable garden overlooking woodlands and farmland.

B&B from £40 single, £70 double, £80 en suite

e-mail: lizzroach@aol.com
Tel: 01491 638309 • Office: 01491 410716
Fax: 01491 638086 • Mobile: 07974714520/1
www.bedbreakfasthenley.co.uk
Self-catering cottage in Rock, Cornwall also available - see:
www.rock-holidaycottage.co.uk

The Close

Guest House

Witney Road

Long Hanborough

Oxfordshire

OX29 8HF

We offer comfortable accommodation in house set in own grounds of one-and-a-half acres. Three family rooms, four double rooms; all en suite; and one double room. Single occupancy by arrangement. All have colour TV and tea/coffee making facilities. Full central heating. Use of garden and car parking for eight cars. Please mention FHG when booking.

Close to Woodstock, Oxford and the Cotswolds.
Open all year except Christmas. Bed and Breakfast from £35.
Mrs I.J. Warwick (01993 882485 • Mob: 07947 023896).

Hill Grove Farm

Crawley Road, Minster Lovell, Witney
Oxon OX29 0NA • 01993 703120

HILL GROVE is a mixed 300-acre working farm situated in an attractive setting with rural views overlooking the River Windrush Valley. Good walking area and easy access to Oxford, Woodstock (Blenheim Palace), Witney, and Burford (Gateway to the Cotswolds and renowned for its Wildlife Park).

Our animals include 2 gorgeous donkeys fostered from the Devon Donkey Sanctuary.

Hearty breakfasts and a warm welcome.

Open all year except Christmas. Non-smoking.

B&B: one double room with private shower £35-£38pp
* one double en suite £37-£39pp * one double/twin en suite £37-£39pp.

Mrs Katharine Brown

e-mail: katharinemcbrown@btinternet.com
www.countryaccom.co.uk/hill-grove-farm

Surrey

Heath • Hall • Farm

Converted stable courtyard surrounded by its own farmland on edge of village of Bowlhead Green. Countryside charming with outstanding walking. Ideal base for many famous historic attractions - Loseley House, Petworth House, Wisley RHS Garden, Arundel Castle, Midhurst (Cowdray Castle), historic Portsmouth. Plenty in locality to visit with children. Central for golf courses; polo at Midhurst. Close to South and North Downs. Relaxed atmosphere in house; domestic pets, cattle, sheep, ducks and chooks.   Wi-Fi

All rooms have en suite bathrooms, Freeview TV, tea/coffee making facilities. Wire-free computer access, security encrypted. Three rooms on ground floor. Guests' sitting room with fridge and microwave oven. Open all year. Children welcome.

Dogs welcome by arrangement • Ample car parking • Warm welcome with friendly help and advice.
Mrs Langdale, Heath Hall Farm, Bowlhead Green, Godalming GU8 6NW •• 01428 682808
e-mail: heathhallfarm@btinternet.com •• www.heathhallfarm.co.uk

The COMPASSES *Inn*
Purveyors of fine food, ale and .....music!

SB

This attractive inn was once known as the 'God Encompasses' but through time and mispronunciation is now simply known as the 'Compasses'.

Known for its appetising selection of home-cooked dishes and supporting local Surrey Hills Brewery, this friendly hostelry has a warm ambience accentuated by its exposed oak beams and horse brasses.

There is good traditional home-cooked food in the bar and the restaurant.
Live music from 9pm every Friday. Situated beneath the North Downs, there is a popular beer garden through which runs the Tillingbourne Stream.

Station Road, Gomshall, Surrey GU5 9LA
Tel: 01483 202 506
www.thecompassesinn.co.uk

Merstham

East Sussex

Alfriston, Eastbourne

Brighton

SB

Wi-Fi

Paskins town house

Distinctive, different, comfortable

PASKINS is a small, green hotel that has found its own way. It's an eclectic, environmentally friendly hotel with nice and sometimes amusing rooms, with the bonus of brilliant breakfasts. You arrive at the Art Nouveau reception to be shown to one of the 19 slightly out of the ordinary rooms, each individual in design, perhaps a little quirky, but not at the expense of being comfortable. For example, one room has a genuine Victorian brass bed with several mattresses, just as Queen Victoria's did, which enabled her to sleep higher than all her subjects. Having been welcomed royally, you will sleep like a monarch, and come down to a regal spread at breakfast, prepared with mainly organic, fair trade or locally sourced produce. The Art Deco breakfast room continues the charming theme of the hotel, and has a menu of celebrated choice, including a variety of imaginative vegetarian and vegan dishes, some intriguing signature dishes, and a blackboard full of specials.

PASKINS TOWN HOUSE • 18/19 Charlotte Street, Brighton BN2 1AG
Tel: 01273 601203 • Fax: 01273 621973
www.paskins.co.uk • welcome@paskins.co.uk

Hastings

West Sussex

Arundel

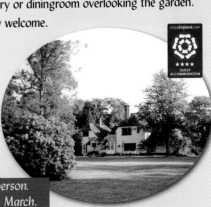

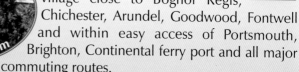

From the dramatic cliffs and sandy beaches of the Sussex coast to the quiet countryside of the Weald and the South Downs, there's an endless choice of the things to do and places to explore. Sailing, walking, cycling, horse riding, golf are all available for an active break, while the fascinating history of 1066 country, castles like Bodiam and the seaside ports will attract all the family. If you're looking for beaches, the 100 miles of coast offer something for everyone, whether your preference is for action-packed fun at a family resort or a quiet, remote spot. Best known for a combination of lively nightlife and all the attractions of the seaside, Brighton has everything from its pebble beach, classic pier, Royal Pavilion and Regency architecture, to shopping malls, art galleries, antique shops, and the specialist boutiques and coffee shops of The Lanes. There's so much to choose from!

THE SQUIRRELS

Albourne Road, Woodmancote, Henfield BN5 9BH

The Squirrels is a country house with lovely large garden set in a secluded area convenient for south coast and downland touring. Brighton and Gatwick 20 minutes. Good food at pub five minutes' walk. One family, one double, one twin and one single rooms, all with colour TV, washbasin, central heating and tea/coffee making facilities. Ample parking space.

A warm welcome awaits you • Open all year.
Directions: from London take M25, M23, A23 towards Brighton, then B2118 to Albourne. Turn right onto B2116 Albourne/Henfield Road – Squirrels is approx. one-and-a-half miles on left.

Tel: 01273 492761
squirrels500@googlemail.com

ST ANDREWS LODGE

Chichester Road, Selsey, West Sussex PO20 0LX
Tel: 01243 606899 • Fax: 01243 607826

Welcome to St Andrews Lodge, the perfect place for a relaxing break. Situated in the small seaside town of Selsey and well located for Chichester and the South Downs; close to unspoilt beaches and 5 minutes from Pagham Harbour Nature Reserve. Enjoy our delicious breakfast and stay in one of our individually decorated rooms. All rooms have hospitality tray and ironing facilities. Fridges in some of the rooms. Some rooms open on to our large garden to allow your dog to stretch his legs. No charge for dogs but donation to local nature reserve welcome. Licensed bar, wheelchair accessible room, large car park.

Please apply for brochure and details of our special winter offer.

info@standrewslodge.co.uk
www.standrewslodge.co.uk

Cambridgeshire

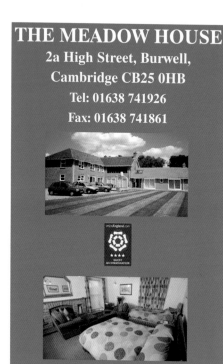

Ely

Stockyard Farm B&B
Wisbech Road, Welney,
Wisbech, Cambridgeshire PE14 9RQ

You are sure to receive a warm welcome from Cindy and Tim when you stay at their cosy farmhouse in the heart of the Fens. Located between Ely and Wisbech, it makes an ideal base from which to explore the numerous local attractions. Whether your interests lie in birdwatching, fishing or visiting historic sites and towns, Stockyard Farm offers a comfortable and convenient retreat.

- Two bedrooms, one double, one twin, both with handbasin, hot drinks facilities and hairdryer • Guest lounge • Conservatory breakfast room, garden and patio • Full central heating • Private parking • Vegetarians and vegans very welcome • Free-range produce • Pets welcome by arrangement - miles of riverside walks • Dogs' breakfast available • Children over 10 years • Non-smoking throughout • B&B from £25.

Mrs C. Bennett
Tel: 01354 610433

Cambridgeshire immediately brings to mind the ancient university city of Cambridge, lazy hours punting on the river past the imposing college buildings, students on bicycles, museums and bookshops. This cosmopolitan centre has so much to offer, with theatres, concerts varying from classical to jazz, an annual music festival, cinemas, botanic gardens, exciting shops and to round it all off, restaurants, pubs and cafes serving high quality food. In the surrounding countryside historic market towns, pretty villages and stately homes wait to be explored. Visit Ely with its magnificent cathedral and museum exhibiting the national collection of stained glass, antique shops and cafes. Shopping is one of the attractions of Peterborough, along with Bronze Age excavations and reconstructed dwelling, a ghost tour of the museum and an annual CAMRA Beer Festival.

Essex

Kelvedon

Highfields Farm

Set in a quiet area on a 700-acre working farm. This makes a peaceful overnight stop on the way to Harwich or a base to visit historic Colchester and Constable country. Convenient for Harwich, Felixstowe and Stansted Airport. Easy access to A12 and main line trains to London.

The accommodation comprises one twin and two double bedrooms, all en suite, with TV and tea/coffee making facilities. Residents' lounge. Good English breakfast is served in the oak beamed dining room.

Wi-Fi

Ample parking • No smoking • Bed and Breakfast from £42-£44 single and £62-£64 twin or double.

Mrs D. Bunting, Highfields Farm, Highfields Lane, Kelvedon CO5 9BJ • Tel & Fax: 01376 570334
e-mail: highfieldsfarm@tiscali.co.uk • www.highfieldsfarm.co.uk

Hertfordshire

Much Hadham

HIGH HEDGES is a family-run B & B in the village of Green Tye, 20 minutes from Stansted Airport, M11, Junction 8 and 5 minutes from the village of Much Hadham.
Accommodation consists of comfortably furnished double/single rooms (cot available on request), all with en-suite or private bathrooms, coffee/tea making facilities, hair dryer and TV.
Local produce is used wherever possible for breakfast. Long stay parking available by arrangement.
We now offer holistic therapies from a qualified therapist. So you can enhance your stay by relaxing and enjoying a luxury therapy to take your mind off the stresses of daily life.

Green Tye, Much Hadham, Herts SG10 6JP
Tel: 01279 842505
e-mail: info@high-hedges.co.uk
www.high-hedges.co.uk

AA
★★★★
Bed & Breakfast

Tall Trees

SB

6 Swallow Close
Nightingale Road
Rickmansworth
WD3 7DZ

Large detached house situated in a quiet cul-de-sac with the centre of Rickmansworth only a short walk away. It is a small picturesque old town where there are many places to eat. We are five minutes' walk from the Underground station, half-an-hour to central London. Convenient for M25 and Watford.

Full breakfast served with homemade bread and preserves. Vegetarians and coeliacs catered for.

Tea and coffee making facilities in rooms. Off-street parking.
No pets. This is a non-smoking household.

Bed and Breakfast from £34.

Mrs Elizabeth Childerhouse - 01923 720069

Hertfordshire's situation just north of London means that visitors based here have the advantage of easy access to all the city's facilities while staying in a pleasant rural environment. This is a county of small, historic market towns and villages with interesting shops, pubs and restaurants serving wonderful food, art galleries and museums explaining the long and fascinating history of this part of Britain. The best known stately houses are Knebworth and Hatfield House. Despite its magnificent Gothic appearance Knebworth hides an original Tudor mansion, and is well worth a visit both for the exterior architecture and the treasures it contains. Perhaps it is best known now as the 'Stately Home of Rock' and is famous worldwide for the concerts held in the grounds. Hatfield House too has Tudor origins and a wing still survives of the Royal Palace of Hatfield where Elizabeth I spent her childhood. The present Jacobean mansion is surrounded by 1000 acres of parkland with trails marked out for pleasant country walks. In contrast, try white water rafting at the new Lee Valley White Water Centre, built for the London 2012 Olympics, and guaranteed to thrill!

Norfolk

SB

Scarning Dale

Comfortable Bed and Breakfast accommodation is available in Dale Cottage. Bedrooms have en suite shower room and hospitality tray.

The 25 acres of pretty countryside surrounding Scarning Dale is a birdwatcher's paradise and an inspiration to painters.
A warm welcome awaits you.

Guests at Scarning Dale may use the heated indoor swimming pool (free use for one hour per day), play snooker (full-size table) or table tennis.

Self-catering accommodation also available.
Dale Road, Scarning,
East Dereham NR19 2QN
Tel: 01362 687269
www.scarningdale.co.uk

THE OLD PUMP HOUSE

Wi-Fi

LUXURY BED & BREAKFAST ACCOMMODATION

This comfortable 1750s house, owned by Marc James and Charles Kirkman, faces the old thatched pump and is a minute from Aylsham's church and historic marketplace.

It offers five en suite bedrooms (including one four-poster and two family rooms) in a relaxed and elegant setting, with colour TV, tea/coffee making facilities, bath robes, hairdryers and CD radio alarm clocks in all rooms. Wireless internet access in all rooms.

English breakfast with free-range eggs and local produce (or vegetarian breakfast) is served in the pine-shuttered sitting room overlooking the peaceful garden.

Aylsham is central for Norwich, the coast, the Broads, National Trust houses, steam railways and unspoilt countryside.

- •Well behaved children welcome. •Non-smoking.
- •Off-road parking for six cars.
- •*B&B: single £80-£98, double/twin £98-£120, family room £123-£145*

Holman Road, Aylsham, Norwich
NR11 6BY
Tel: 01263 733789
theoldpumphouse@btconnect.com
www.theoldpumphouse.com

Hempstead Hall

Holt, Norfolk NR25 6TN

Enjoy a relaxing holiday with a friendly atmosphere in our 19th century flint farmhouse, beautifully set on a 300 acre arable farm with ducks, donkey and large gardens. Close to the north Norfolk coast and its many attractions. Take a ride on the steam train or a boat trip to Blakeney Point Seal Sanctuary.

Large en suite family room, double with private bathroom. Colour TV, tea/coffee facilities. Large dining room with log burning stove. Children over 12 years only, please. Sorry, no pets indoors.

B&B from £32-£35 per person.

Tel: 01263 712224 • www.hempsteadhall.co.uk

Woodgreen, Long Stratton
Norwich NR15 2RR

SB

Greenacres Farmhouse

Period 17th century farmhouse on 30 acre common with ponds and natural wildlife, 10 miles south of Norwich (A140). The beamed sittingroom with inglenook fireplace invites you to relax. A large sunny dining room encourages you to enjoy a leisurely traditional breakfast. All en suite bedrooms (two double/twin) are tastefully furnished to complement the oak beams and period furniture, with tea/coffee facilities and TV. Full size snooker table and all-weather tennis court for guests' use. Jo is trained in therapeutic massage, pilates and reflexology and is able to offer this to guests who feel it would be of benefit. Come and enjoy the peace and tranquillity of our home.

Bed and Breakfast from £30. Reductions for two nights or more. Non-smoking.

Tel: 01508 530261 • www.abreakwithtradition.co.uk

Norwich, Spalding (Lincolnshire)

SB
Wi-Fi

SOUTH NORFOLK GUEST HOUSE

This former village school, set in the heart of Norfolk's unspoilt countryside, is an ideal location from which to explore East Anglia.

As a professionally run guest house, a comfortable stay is guaranteed, complemented by a delicious breakfast with locally sourced products.

FRITH WAY, GT. MOULTON, NORWICH, NR15 2HE
WWW.SOUTHNORFOLKGUESTHOUSE.CO.UK   (01379) 677359

THE HARBOUR VIEW
BED & BREAKFAST | RESTAURANT | WEDDINGS | CONFERENCES

The Harbour View is a Victorian Farmhouse with converted barns, combining a taste of the countryside with the modern facilities required by families and business people alike. Set on the banks of the River Nene, we are within easy reach of Sandringham and are situated on the fringes of The Wash, home to some of the most diverse wildlife in the UK.

We offer 11 modern bedrooms - Standard, Executive and Family rooms. The feature rooms are our fabulously decorated four-poster bedrooms, some of which enjoy fantastic views over the stunning Lincolnshire countryside.

There is a small leisure facility on the ground floor, with fitness equipment, pool table and sauna. This is complimentary to all hotel guests. Wi-Fi available in bedrooms and public areas.

We are a family-friendly hotel and welcome children of all ages. Although we do not accept pets in the rooms we can accommodate cats and dogs in our secure kennels.

The Harbour View
East Bank Farm, Garners Lane, Sutton Bridge,
Spalding, Lincolnshire PE12 9YP
Telephone: 01406 351 333 • www.theharbourview.co.uk

WROXHAM. Wroxham Park Lodge, 142 Norwich Road, Wroxham NR12 8SA (01603 782991).
Friendly Bed and Breakfast in an elegant Victorian house in Wroxham, part of the Norfolk Broads, England's magical waterways. All rooms en suite, TV, radio, tea/coffee. Famed hearty breakfasts. Large garden with patio, car park. Ideal for touring Norfolk, boat trips and hire, walking, cycling, fishing, steam railways, gardens, zoos and historic houses. Near North Norfolk coast, Norwich and Great Yarmouth.
Rates: Bed and Breakfast from £33 per person.
• Non-smoking • Open all year
VisitBritain ★★★★.

e-mail: parklodge@computer-assist.net   www.wroxhamparklodge.com

Home Farm

Comfortable accommodation set in four acres, quiet location, secluded garden. Conveniently situated off A11 between Attleborough and Wymondham, an excellent location for Snetterton and only 20 minutes from Norwich and 45 minutes from the Norfolk Broads.

Accommodation comprises two double rooms and one single-bedded room, all with TV, tea/coffee facilities and central heating. Children over five years old welcome, but sorry no animals and no smoking. Fishing lakes only ½ mile away.

Bed and Breakfast from £30pppn.

Mrs Joy Morter, Home Farm, Morley, Wymondham NR18 9US
Tel: 01953 602581

Along the Norfolk coast from King's Lynn to Great Yarmouth the broad, sandy beaches, grassy dunes, nature reserves, windmills, and pretty little fishing villages are inviting at all times of year. Following the routes of the Norfolk Coastal Path and Norfolk Coast Cycle Way, walk or cycle between the picturesque villages, stopping to visit the interesting shops and galleries, or to enjoy the seafood at a traditional pub or a restaurant. Take lessons in surfing at Wells-next-the-Sea, then enjoy the challenge of the waves at East Runton or Cromer, or go sea fishing here, or at Sheringham or Mundesley. An important trade and fishing port from medieval times, the historic centre of King's Lynn is well worth a visit, and take a break at Great Yarmouth for family entertainment, 15 miles of sandy beaches, traditional piers, a sea life centre and nightlife with clubs and a casino.

Bungay

Suffolk

Suffolk's 40 miles of unspoilt World Heritage coastline is perfect for a seaside holiday. Whether you're looking for a quiet weekend break or an active family fortnight in a well established resort, a music festival - rock and pop or classical, farm parks and fun parks or just to indulge in the wonderful local food, it's all to be found here. Wander through the coastal forests or along the shingle and sandy beaches admiring the scenery, or hire bicycles for a family bike ride. Rent a gaily painted beach hut at Felixstowe, where the level esplanade and beaches are ideal both for small children and older family members, try crabs fresh from the sea at Walberswick, or enjoy the annual music and literature festivals at Aldeburgh. Eat oysters at Orford, and explore the Norman castle, or follow the Suffolk Coastal Churches Trail.

SB

HIGH HOUSE FARM

Farmhouse Bed & Breakfast

High House Farm is a family-run farm in the heart of rural Suffolk, offering quality Bed & Breakfast in our 15th Century listed farmhouse.

Featuring: exposed oak beams • inglenook fireplaces • generous Full English Breakfast with locally sourced ingredients • tea and coffee making facilities • flat screen TVs • one double room, en suite and one large family room with double and twin beds and private adjacent bathroom
children's cots • high chairs • books • toys • outside play equipment • attractive semi-moated gardens • farm and woodland walks.

Explore the heart of rural Suffolk, local vineyard, Easton Farm Park, Framlingham and Orford Castles, Parham Air Museum, Saxtead Windmill, Minsmere, Snape Maltings, Woodland Trust.

High House Farm

Cransford, Framlingham, Woodbridge IP13 9PD
Tel: 01728 663461
e-mail: b&b@highhousefarm.co.uk www.highhousefarm.co.uk

SB

At Woodbridge visit the Tide Mill and Buttrum's Mill, the tallest remaining windmill in Suffolk, and the nearby Anglo-Saxon burial site at Sutton Hoo. River yachting is another option, and of course right along the coast there are opportunities for all forms of boating, sailing, and diving holidays. Fishing is particularly popular on the Waveney and on many other rivers as well, and there are plenty of opportunities for still water angling or sea fishing too. Golfers are not neglected, with a choice between short local courses to some of championship standard, with luxury hotel accommodation on site. Horse racing enthusiasts can't miss Newmarket, whether for a fun day out, to visit the National Horseracing Museum or to take a guided tour round the National Stud.

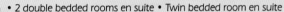

The Old Rectory is a Listed building dating from the 16th century, well situated to explore East Anglia, being on the Suffolk/Norfolk border. Bury St Edmunds is 12 miles away, the market town of Diss is 8. Cambridge, Ipswich and Norwich are within easy reach. The house is beautifully furnished and many period features add to the charm of this lovely stylish family home.
Sarah and Bobby delight in entertaining guests in their beautifully restored home.

Gold AWARD

- 2 double bedded rooms en suite • Twin bedded room en suite
- Continental/English Breakfast
- Dinner available by arrangement. • Licensed
- Children welcome by arrangement
- Dogs welcome by arrangement (extra £10.00)
- Drawing Room with unique rotunda • Next to church
- No smoking house • Large garden • Croquet
- Closed Christmas, New Year and occasionally at other times.
- Credit/debit cards not accepted

**Bobby & Sarah Llewellyn, The Old Rectory
Hopton, Suffolk IP22 2QX • Tel: 01953 688135
e-mail: llewellyn.hopton@btinternet.com
www.theoldrectoryhopton.com**

SB

Sweffling Hall Farm

Set well back from the main Framlingham-Saxmundham road, in a quiet location with pond and garden. We have chickens providing free-range eggs. Convenient for Woodland Trust (nearby), Framlingham Castle, Saxstead Mill and Coast. Only 9 miles away is Aldeburgh and Minsmere Bird Reserve. Ideal for walking and cycling; vintage transport can be provided free for those staying longer. Two double rooms with private/en suite bathroom and a family room with one double bed and two single beds. There is also a garden with a large pond that can be viewed from the family room.

SWEFFLING HALL FARM
Sweffling, Saxmundham IP17 2BT
Tel & Fax: 01728 663644
e-mail: stephen.mann@hotmail.co.uk
www.swefflinghallfarm.co.uk

A warm welcome awaits you at our exceptional moated farmhouse dating from the 13th Century, and set in extensive grounds including Ace all weather tennis court, in a superb spot two and a half miles north of Dennington, 13 miles from Woodbridge. A comfortable base with log fires in winter and plenty of beams. Close to Snape Maltings, the coast, Minsmere and many places of interest. Accommodation comprises one double and one twin bedroom, or two twins let as singles; guests' own bathroom and sitting room. Good pubs nearby. Bread and marmalade home made.

Parking available • Non-smoking.
B&B from £34 Single, £68 Double/Twin.

GRANGE FARM
Dennington, Woodbridge IP13 8BT
Tel: 01986 798388 • mobile: 07774 182835
www.grangefarm.biz

Derbyshire

Stone Cottage

A charming cottage in the quiet village of Clifton, one mile from the Georgian market town of Ashbourne. Each bedroom is furnished to a high standard with all rooms en suite, one with four-poster bed; TV and coffee making facilities. A warm welcome is assured and a hearty breakfast in this delightful cottage. There is a large garden to relax in. Ideal for visiting Chatsworth House, Haddon Hall, Dovedale, Carsington Water and the theme park of Alton Towers.

B&B from £28pp. Good country pubs nearby serving evening meals.

Enquiries to: Mrs A. M. Whittle, Stone Cottage, Green Lane, Clifton, Ashbourne, Derbyshire DE6 2BL • Tel/Fax: 01335 343377
e-mail: info@stone-cottage.fsnet.co.uk

Compton House
Guest House in Ashbourne

Compton House is situated in the charming historic market town of Ashborne, with its fine Georgian architecture. We are a family-run guest house with accent on good food and accommodation, and a warm friendly atmosphere.

There are five bedrooms, all en suite, with colour TV, radio, and hairdryer, plus a well stocked tea and coffee tray. All rooms have double beds, and the two larger rooms also have a single bed, so can be used as twin or family rooms. Two rooms can be let as single rooms if required; one of the double rooms is on the ground floor overlooking the garden. Free Wi-Fi.

From peaks to dales to caverns, pretty thatched cottages to majestic stately homes, steam trains to boating lakes, rolling green fields to rocky crags, rivers to streams; whether you want to drive, or ride, walk or climb, cycle or sail, all are on offer in the beautiful Peak District Countryside.

Rooms from £40 to £85 per night

27-31 Compton, Ashbourne DE6 1BX
Tel: 01335 343100
e-mail: jane@comptonhouse.co.uk • www.comptonhouse.co.uk

Throwley Hall Farm

Peak District B&B at Ilam, Ashbourne, Derbyshire

enjoyEngland.com

★★★★
FARMHOUSE

Holiday accommodation on a working beef cattle farm in a beautiful area of the Peak District National Park

Throwley Hall Farm is a Georgian farmhouse conveniently situated in the quiet countryside near to the beautiful Manifold Valley and Dovedale.

Superb scenery and walking country are right on the doorstep, and attractions such as Alton Towers are a short journey away.

- 4 double/twin rooms (3 en suite).
- Dining/sitting room with TV.
- Tea/coffee making.
- Full central heating.
- Open fire.
- Terms from £32pppn.
- Reduced rates for children.
- Cot and high chair available.

Self-catering accommodation also available in farmhouse and cottages. ETC ★★★★

Ilam, Ashbourne, Derbyshire DE6 2BB • Tel: 01538 308202/308243

e-mail: throwleyhall@btinternet.com • www.throwleyfarm.co.uk

Guests are warmly welcomed into the friendly atmosphere of Braemar, situated in a quiet residential part of this famous spa town. Within five minutes' walk of all the town's many and varied attractions:

SB

Pavilion Gardens, Opera House, swimming pool; golf courses, horse riding, walking, fishing, etc are all within easy reach in this area renowned for its scenic beauty. Many of the Peak District's famous beauty spots including Chatsworth, Haddon Hall, Bakewell, Matlock, Dovedale and Castleton are nearby.

Wi-Fi

Accommodation comprises comfortable double and twin bedded rooms fully en suite with colour TV and hospitality trays. Free Wi-Fi available. Full English Breakfast served and diets catered for. Non-smokers preferred.

Terms from £27.50 inclusive for Bed and Breakfast. Weekly terms available.

Braemar

Roger and Maria Hyde
10 Compton Road, Buxton SK17 9DN
Tel: 01298 78050 • e-mail: buxtonbraemar@supanet.com
www.cressbrook.co.uk/buxton/braemar

The Clarendon Guest House

SB

Located near the town centre and within easy reach of the Peak District, this Victorian town house offers a warm and cheerful welcome, whether on business or pleasure. Comfortable, cosy rooms, each with TV and tea/coffee facilities. The rear walled garden offers a peaceful summer retreat. Full English breakfast; special diets catered for.

Bed and Breakfast from £25 single, from £50 double/twin room en suite.

Mr & Mrs A. Boardman, The Clarendon Guest House, 32 Clarence Road, Chesterfield S40 1LN (01246 235004) www.clarendonguesthouse.com

For walking, climbing, cycling, horse riding, mountain biking and caving, visit Derbyshire. Take part in one of the walking festivals, with themed walks at every level, cycle the recently restored Monsal Trail through spectacular scenery along the old railway line from Bakewell to Buxton, or hire an electric bike to enjoy the countryside, whatever your level of fitness. Visit Poole's Cavern to see the best stalagmites and stalactites in Derbyshire (and discover the difference!), and the Blue John Cave at Castleton where this rare mineral is mined, and perhaps buy a sample of jewellery in one of the local shops. Buxton was a spa from Roman times, but the main attractions now are concerts, theatre and the opera, music and literature festival held every year.

Castleton

SB

Wi-Fi

Causeway House B&B

Back Street, Castleton, Hope Valley S33 8WE
01433 623291 • email: info@causewayhouse.co.uk
www.causewayhouse.co.uk

Come and Stay in our delightful
15th Century Cruck Cottage

Causeway House is a gem.
Comfortable accommodation with all the
conveniences of the 21st century in a 15th
century cruck cottage with huge original oak
timbers that ooze history.

Whether you're staying for a single night or a
whole week, Janet and Nick Steynberg will make
sure your stay is an unforgettable experience; one
you'll want to return to again and again.

We have five bedrooms, three luxurious en suite
rooms and two with shared facilities, all tastefully
decorated, with hospitality tray, colour TV, clock
radio and hairdryer. Our Garden Room is on
the ground floor and is ideal for guests who
prefer to avoid stairs, although there are a
couple of steps to access it.
Our stunning four-poster room just oozes
history and character and our double room is a
perfect place to relax.
Breakfasts are a treat, with a choice between a full
English and lighter alternatives.

SB

*A warm welcome
on the edge of the
Peak District*

Graham and Julie Caesar

Windy Harbour Farm Hotel

Woodhead Road, Glossop SK13 7QE
01457 853107 • www.peakdistrict-hotel.co.uk
e-mail: enquiries@peakdistrict-hotel.co.uk

Situated in the heart of the Peak District on the B6105, approximately one mile
from Glossop town centre and adjacent to the Pennine Way.

All our bedrooms are en suite, with outstanding views of Woodhead and Snake
Passes, and the Longdendale Valley is an ideal location for all outdoor activities.

A warm welcome awaits you in our licensed bar and restaurant serving
a wide range of excellent home-made food.

Bed and Breakfast from £30 per night

Winster

Leicestershire & Rutland

Belton-in-Rutland

Lincolnshire

Coast or country, the choice is yours for a holiday in Lincolnshire. With award-winning beaches, miles of clean sand, theme parks, kite surfing, jet skiing and seaside nature reserves, there's action, excitement and interests for everyone right along the coast. At Skegness, as well as all the fun on the beach, children will love watching the seals being fed at the seal sanctuary, and the Parrot Zoo nearby. There's a seal sanctuary at Mablethorpe too, and all the fun of the fairground, as well as beach huts to hire if the sun goes behind a cloud. Further north, at Cleethorpes with its wonderful beaches and Pleasure Island, take a ride on the Cleethorpes Coast Light Railway, or a guided tour of the sand dunes and saltmarshes at the Discovery Centre to find out about local wildlife habitats.

WEST WOLD FARM HOUSE

We welcome you to our small, friendly, family-run farmhouse in the delightful hamlet of Deepdale, to enjoy the comfort of our home and garden.

Our rooms have en suite or private bathroom, tea/coffee making facilities, TV, radio and hairdryer. Trouser press, iron and board, wet outdoor clothes drying facilities available. We offer the 'Great British' breakfast, with fresh, locally sourced produce where possible; vegetarian and other diets as requested.

We are central for visiting Hull, Beverley, Lincoln and York, and close to historic Barton. There is a SSSI, 3 miles away on the Humber Estuary, and we are 200 yards from a bridleway, leading to a network of bridleways and the Viking Way. Dogs and horses welcome by arrangement. We have plenty of off-road parking.

Terms from £29.00 single to £64 double en suite pppn.
Special breaks and long term discounts available.

Mrs. Pam Atkin, West Wold Farmhouse
Deepdale, Barton-upon-Humber, North Lincs DN18 6ED
Tel: 01652 633293 / 07889 532937
e-mail: pam@westwoldfarmhouse.co.uk
www.westwoldfarmhouse.co.uk

Ground floor accommodation in chalet-type house. Central for Wolds, coast, fens, historic Lincoln. Market towns, Louth, Horncastle, Boston, Spilsby, Alford, Woodhall Spa. Two double bedrooms. Washbasin, TV; bathroom, toilet adjoining; lounge with colour TV, separate dining room. Drinks provided. Children welcome reduced rates. Car almost essential, parking. Numerous eating places nearby. B&B from £30 per person (double/single let). Open all year. Tourist Board Listed. Pets welcome free.

MISS JESSIE SKELLERN, LEA HOLME, LANGTON-BY-WRAGBY, LINCOLN LN8 5PZ (01673 858339)

KEDDINGTON HOUSE • "Host Home"
5 Keddington Road, Louth LN11 0AA
Tel: 01507 603973 • Mobile: 0781 8290990

Tony Moss offers:

• A large Victorian house, set in its own grounds 100 yards back from the road, with extensive parking.

• Double/twin/single and family en suite rooms

• Separate lounges with tea/coffee/biscuits always available

• Heated outdoor swimming pool (summer months only)

• Easy access to Louth town centre – Lincolnshire Wolds

Ideally placed for Lincoln, Grimsby and Market Rasen Racecourse. Within half-an-hour of the seaside at Mablethorpe and Skegness. Cadwell Park 10 minutes away - early breakfasts if required.

e-mail: tony@keddingtonhouse.co.uk
www.keddingtonhouse.co.uk

Bed & Breakfast at No. 19 West Street
Kings Cliffe, Near Stamford, Peterborough PE8 6XB
Tel: 01780 470365 • Fax: 01780 470623

A beautifully restored 500-year-old Listed stone house, reputedly one of King John's Hunting Lodges, situated in the heart of the stone village of Kings Cliffe on the edge of Rockingham Forest. Within 20 miles there are seven stately homes, including Burghley House famous for the Horse Trials, Rutland Water, and the beautiful old towns of Stamford and Oundle.

Both the double and twin rooms have their own private bathrooms, and there is colour TV and a welcome tray in each. In the summer breakfast can be served on the terrace overlooking a beautiful walled garden. There is also a completely self-contained family suite, can be self-catering. Off-street parking is behind secure gates. Open all year.

A non-smoking house • Bed and Breakfast from £30 per person (2 sharing) • Proprietor: Jenny Dixon
e-mail: kjhl.dixon@gmail.com • www.kingjohnhuntinglodge.co.uk

Redhurst B&B & Self-Catering

Exchange the buzz of city traffic for the birdsong of the countryside whilst staying at Redhurst B&B, set in gardens and orchard in a small village nestling on the edge of the Lincolnshire Wolds. Ideal setting for visiting the many and varied attractions of Lincolnshire.

Two twin en suite (one ground floor).
From £28 and £31pppn.
One single with private facilities. From £28pn.
Open all year • Sorry no pets • Non-smoking
• Self-catering also available in house and in "The Shed", sleeps 4.

SB
&
Wi-Fi

**Mrs Vivienne Klockner, Redhurst,
Holton-cum-Beckering,
Market Rasen LN8 5NG
Tel: 01673 857927
www.RedhurstBAndB.co.uk
e-mail: Vivienne@RedhurstBAndB.co.uk**

Northamptonshire

Northamptonshire may appear a quiet, rural county, but it's very much a place for action and family fun. Everything you would expect to find in the countryside is here – walking, cycling, fishing, wildlife, castles and stately homes steeped in history, beautiful villages and traditional inns and pubs. As well as all this motorsports enthusiasts will be more than satisfied, with stock car racing at the Northampton International Raceway, Santa Pod, the home of European Drag Racing and the Silverstone circuit. For shoppers, Northampton, the home of high quality footwear in Britain, is still a good place for bargains as well as bespoke shoes, and for some fun, why not end the holiday with a visit to Wicksteed Park at Kettering where you'll find all the family could want in events and entertainment.

Burton Joyce

Nottinghamshire

Willow House Bed and Breakfast

A period house (1857) in quiet village two minutes' walk from beautiful river bank, yet only five miles from City. Attractive, interesting accommodation with authentic Victorian ambience. En suite available. Bright, clean rooms with tea/coffee facilities, TV.
Off-road parking. Porch for smokers.
Ideally situated for Holme Pierrepont International Watersports Centre; golf; National Ice Centre; Trent Bridge (cricket); Sherwood Forest; Nottingham Racecourse; Shelford Pony Trials and the unspoiled historic town of Southwell with its Minster and Racecourse.
Good local eating. Please phone first for directions.
Rates: From £26 per person per night.

**Mrs V. Baker, Willow House,
Burton Joyce NG14 5FD
Tel:0115 931 2070; Mob: 07816 347706
www.willowhousebedandbreakfast.co.uk**

In Nottinghamshire the myths, legends and facts all play a part in the stories of Robin Hood, but visit Sherwood Forest, the hiding place of outlaws in medieval times, and make up your own mind from the evidence you find there. Watch cricket at Trent Bridge, horse racing at Nottingham and the all-weather course at Southwell, and ice hockey at Nottingham's National Ice Centre, or try ice skating yourself. There are golf courses from municipal and pay & play to championship standard, fishing in canals, lakes and fisheries, walking by rivers and canals and cycling in the woodland and country parks, and everyone is welcome to play at the Nottingham Tennis Centre. The city of Nottingham is a wonderful place to shop, with designer outlets, independent shops and department stores, and don't miss the traditional Lace Market.

SB

Everything at Andrews Hotel is done with a view to making your stay enjoyable and relaxing. Friendly atmosphere and a sense of home-from-home. All rooms have colour TV, tea/coffee and washbasins, some are en suite. Within easy reach of the Derbyshire Dales and Robin Hood country. Situated on the west side of Nottingham, 10 minutes from the city centre; also close by is Nottingham Tennis Centre and University.

Prices start at £28 basic single, and £25 per person for a twin/double room including breakfast.

**Peter and Josephine Howat,
Andrews Guest House,
310 Queens Road, Beeston,
Nottingham NG9 1JA
0115 9254902**

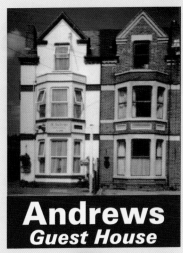

Andrews
Guest House

SB

Wi-Fi

**e-mail: andrews.hotel@ntlworld.com
www.andrewshotelnottingham.com**

Dalestorth Guest House is an 18th century Georgian family home converted in the 19th century to become a school for young ladies of the local gentry and a boarding school until the 1930s. In 1976 it was bought by the present owners and has been modernised and converted into a comfortable, clean and pleasant guest house serving the areas of Mansfield and Sutton-in-Ashfield, offering overnight accommodation of Bed and Breakfast or longer stays to businessmen, holidaymakers or friends and relations visiting the area. From £20 per person per night.

SB

**Mr P. Jordan, Dalestorth Guest House,
Skegby Lane, Skegby,
Sutton-in-Ashfield NG17 3DH
Tel: 01623 551110 • Fax: 01623 442241
www.dalestorth.co.uk**

Burghill, Hereford

Herefordshire

Outdoor activities, creative arts and crafts, wonderful food - Herefordshire, on the border with Wales, will appeal whatever your interest. With its rolling countryside and green meadows dotted with woodland and meandering streams, there are endless opportunities for all kinds of outdoor activities, from white water canoeing on the Yat Rapids through the steep-sided gorge at Symonds Yat, to longer, more gentle trips on the quieter sections of the River Wye. Footpaths, bridleways and cycle trails through countryside rich in wildlife are perfect for families as well as the more experienced. The Black and White Village Trail takes visitors through beautiful countryside to pretty little villages, each with its own individual characteristics and shops, or follow the Cider Route in this county of apple orchards.

SB

Wi-Fi

Thatch Close Farm
Bed & Breakfast
Llangrove, Ross on Wye

Situated between the Black Mountains
and the Wye Valley, with marvellous
views from every angle,
Thatch Close is the ideal location for a
weekend break or a longer stay.

Secluded, peaceful, comfortable
Georgian farmhouse, yet convenient for
A40, M4 and M50. Our three lovely
bedrooms, all en suite, have
magnificent views over the unspoilt
countryside. Relax in the visitors'
lounge or sit in the shade of mature
trees in our garden. You may be greeted
by our dog or free-flying parrot. Terms
from £32.50-£55. Children and dogs are
welcome. Please telephone
or e-mail for brochure.

Thatch Close Bed & Breakfast, LLangrove, Ross-on-Wye HR9 6EL

Mrs M.E. Drzymalski (01989 770300)

e-mail: info@thatchclose.co.uk • www.thatchclose.co.uk

Ross-on-Wye

Shropshire

SB

Wi-Fi

Lovely 16th century farmhouse in peaceful village amidst the beautiful South Shropshire Hills, where Victorian Farm was filmed, an Area of Outstanding Natural Beauty. The farmhouse is full of character and all rooms have heating and are comfortable and spacious. The bedrooms are either en suite or private bathroom with hairdryers, tea/coffee making facilities, patchwork quilts and colour TV. There is a lounge with colour TV and inglenook fireplace. Children welcome. We are a working farm, centrally situated for visiting Ironbridge, Shrewsbury and Ludlow, each being easily reached within half an hour. Touring and walking information is available for visitors. Bed and full English Breakfast from £29pppn. Non-smoking. Open all year excluding November, December, January and February.

Mrs Mary Jones, Acton Scott Farm, Acton Scott, Church Stretton SY6 6QN • Tel: 01694 781260
Fax: 0870-129 4591 • e-mail: fhg@actonscottfarm.co.uk • www.actonscottfarm.co.uk

Wi-Fi

Mynd House

Bed and Breakfast in an Edwardian Guest House near Church Stretton in Shropshire

An Edwardian house built at the turn of the century, it provides 7 spacious en suite bedrooms with stunning views of the surrounding Shropshire hills - an ideal location for pleasure or business.

All the spacious en suite bedrooms, including a four-poster suite and a de luxe family room, have TV, mini-bar fridge and tea/coffee making. Wi-Fi available. Licensed residents' bar.

Many National Trust and other historic properties are within easy reach.

Mynd House, Ludlow Road, Little Stretton,
Church Stretton, Shropshire SY6 6RB
Tel: 01694 722212 • www.myndhouse.co.uk
e-mail: info@myndhouse.co.uk

Family-run B&B with 7 en suite bedrooms
Comfortable guest lounge
Residential licensed bar

Ludlow

If you're looking for a break from the pace of life today, but with plenty to do and see,
Shropshire is the place to visit. For the active visitor the quiet countryside bordering on the
Welsh Marches offers opportunities for walking, cycling, horse riding, kayaking, canoeing,
and quad and mountain biking, while if the history of the region's turbulent past appeals,
there are over 30 castles to visit, as well as stately homes and beautiful gardens. Visit the
grass-roofed Shropshire Hills Discovery Centre at Craven Arms, where you can take a
simulated balloon ride and meet the Shropshire mammoth, and Stokesay Castle, the finest
13th century fortified manor house in England. To find out about the more recent past visit
the ten museums at the Ironbridge Gorge.

Telford

SB

Wi-Fi

The Mill House

Bed & Breakfast in an 18th Century Converted Water Mill

Judy and Chris Yates welcome you to The Mill House, an 18th century converted water mill situated beside the River Roden on a 9-acre working smallholding in the village of High Ercall, halfway between the historic county town of Shrewsbury and the new town of Telford.

Perfect for exploring Shropshire and the Welsh borderlands; a short distance from the World Heritage Site of the Ironbridge Gorge. The surrounding area offers a wide range of attractions and activities to suit all tastes.

Luxury B&B accommodation in three beautifully decorated bedrooms: two double/twin rooms, both en suite and one family room en suite. All rooms have colour TV with Freeview and DVD. There is a large dining room and lounge area for guests.

Wi-Fi internet access available.
Children welcome
Dogs accepted by prior arrangement
Single £39pn, Double/Twin £28pppn,
Family room (sleeps 4) from £24 pppn.

Shrewsbury Road, High Ercall, Telford TF6 6BE
Tel: 01952 770394
e-mail: judy@ercallmill.co.uk • www.ercallmill.co.uk

Staffordshire

SB

Wi-Fi

Stafford

Situated right in the middle of England, for an active holiday Staffordshire is difficult to beat. There are forest walks and cycle trails for all the family in the National Forest and over the historic heathlands and woodlands of Cannock Chase, and everything from canoeing to climbing in the Staffordshire Peak District. The exciting theme parks, stately homes and castles, miles of canals and the largest street-style skate park in Europe at Stoke-on-Trent, ensure thrills, interest and fun for every age group. Take a look at life in the past at the complete working historic estate at Shugborough near Stafford, with working kitchens, dairy water mill and brewhouse, shop at the retail village or walk with the monkeys in Trentham's historic estate or just take a leisurely boat trip down one of the many canals, there's so much of interest to see and do!

Warwickshire

Stratford-Upon-Avon

West Midlands

Wolverhampton

Worcestershire

Droitwich Spa

East Yorkshire

SB

With family-friendly beaches, dramatic coastal cliffs and the gentle uplands of the Wolds inland, East Yorkshire will appeal to all age groups and interests. Following one of the many walking trails through the quiet and beautiful countryside, ramblers will discover hidden valleys and traditional villages and market towns like Beverley, with its medieval centre, 13th century Minster, and literature, jazz and folk festivals. Driffield, known as the capital of the Wolds, is an ideal centre from which to explore both countryside and coast, or for a seaside holiday with golden sands, award-winning promenades and entertainment of all kinds at the Spa, Bridlington is ideal for a family break. Take the land train up to the top of the spectacular cliffs, summer home to huge seabird colonies, try kite-flying in the North Sea breezes, or play a round of golf on the clifftop links.

Beverley

ROBEANNE HOUSE

Bed & Breakfast

Wi-Fi

A friendly, informal and comfortable guest house, conveniently located for York, the Wolds and the East Coast. The accommodation we offer includes either spacious comfortable suites in the main guest house or luxury log cabins situated within our extensive gardens. All our rooms are non smoking.

Whether here for a holiday, a romantic break or on business, we can offer you a quiet country location whilst still being accessible to the surrounding areas.

The rooms in the main house and cottage are either twin bedded or king-size. They are all very pleasantly decorated and equipped, with en suite facilities with shower, welcome pack of tea, coffee, hot chocolate and biscuits, books, colour television/DVD, hairdryer and ironing facilities. Each room also has a breathtaking countryside view.
We also have a family suite, ideal for larger parties or the larger family, equipped with two bedrooms, and a bathroom with shower. Our log cabins are well equipped, with en suite facilities with shower, colour television/DVD, hairdryer and ironing facilities.
They also have a balcony with sitting area overlooking the lovely, peaceful, garden.

Towthorpe Lane, Shiptonthorpe, York YO43 3PW
Tel: 01430 873312 • e-mail: enquiries@robeannehouse.co.uk
www.robeannehouse.co.uk

Carperby, Coverdale

North Yorkshire

Danby

Wi-Fi

Rowantree Farm

ROWANTREE FARM is a family-run dairy farm situated in the heart of the North York Moors. Ideal walking and mountain biking area, with panoramic moorland views. Coast easily accessible.
Our non-smoking home comprises one family room and one twin-bedded room, with private bathroom and private shower room, also full central heating, beverage tray, CD clock radio and hairdryer.
Relax in our residents' lounge with colour TV. Ample car parking.

Children welcome, cot and high chair available

Great farmhouse breakfast (vegetarians catered for) served in our separate dining room

B&B from £28

Mrs L. Tindall, Rowantree Farm, Ainthorpe, Whitby YO21 2LE
Tel: 01287 660396 • e-mail: krbsatindall@aol.com
www.rowantreefarm.co.uk

Dominated by the magnificent York Minster, the largest medieval Gothic cathedral in northern Europe, the city of York in North Yorkshire is full of attractions for the visitor. Have fun finding your way through the Snickelways, the maze of hidden alleyways, and enjoy a morning – or longer – in the array of independent shops and boutiques as well as all the top high street stores. Explore York's past at Jorvik, the recreation of the original Viking city from 1000 years ago or become an archaeologist for the day at Dig! and excavate for yourself items from Viking, Roman, medieval and Victorian times. Outside the city the vast open stretches of the North York Moors and Yorkshire Dales National Parks and the golden sandy beaches of the coast are perfect for an active holiday.

Sunnyridge

ARGILL FARM, HARMBY, LEYBURN DL8 5HQ
Tel: 01969 622478 • Mrs Hilary Richardson
e-mail: Hilary@safarm.co.uk
www.sunnyridgeargillfarm.co.uk

Situated on a small sheep farm in Wensleydale, near the market town of Leyburn, Sunnyridge is a spacious bungalow in an outstanding position. Magnificent views are enjoyed from every room. In the heart of the Yorkshire Dales near The Forbidden Corner, it is an ideal centre for exploring the wide variety of activities and attractions; or a restful stop-over for travellers.

We offer spacious accommodation comprising double, twin or family bedrooms with en suite facilities, colour TV, hairdryer and tea/coffee making equipment. All rooms have full central heating, and double glazing. We also offer private car parking. Guests are encouraged to make themselves feel at home, to relax and enjoy their pleasant surroundings.

Sample our delicious farmhouse breakfast and, after a good day's walking or touring, unwind and prepare for the next day in our spacious, comfortable residents' lounge.

FARMHOUSE

Pets by arrangement • B&B from £30

SB

THE OLD STAR
West Witton, Leyburn
DL8 4LU
Tel: 01969 622949
enquiries@theoldstar.com
www.theoldstar.com

Formerly a 17th century coaching inn, now a family-run guest house, you are always welcome at the Old Star.

The building still retains many original features. Comfortable lounge with oak beams and log fire. Bedrooms mostly en suite with central heating, TV and tea/coffee making facilities.

Two good food pubs in village. In the heart of the Yorkshire Dales National Park we are ideally situated for walking and touring the Dales. Large car park. Open all year except Christmas.

GUEST ACCOMMODATION

En suite Bed and Breakfast from £29pppn.

SB

Dominated by the magnificent York Minster, the largest medieval Gothic cathedral in northern Europe, the city of York in North Yorkshire is full of attractions for the visitor. Outside the city the vast open stretches of the North York Moors and Yorkshire Dales National Parks and the golden sandy beaches of the coast are perfect for an active holiday. Every standard of fitness and ability is catered for, whether surfing at Scarborough or cycling through Dalby Forest, gliding over the North York Moors National Park or floating in a hot air balloon admiring the scenery at dawn. Gentle, short, circular routes for walkers are centred on interesting, historic stone villages and busy market towns, or cross the countryside on the more demanding long distance trails, like the Cleveland Way, the Pennine Trail and the Dales Way, or the challenging Yorkshire Three Peaks in Ribblesdale.

Pickering

Banavie
Bed & Breakfast

Holiday Accommodation in Thornton-Le-Dale, Pickering, Yorkshire

A large semi-detached house set in a quiet part of the picturesque village of Thornton-le-Dale, one of the prettiest villages in Yorkshire with its famous thatched cottage and bubbling stream flowing through the centre.

We offer our guests a quiet night's sleep and rest away from the main road, yet only four minutes' walk from the village centre.

One large double or twin bedroom and two double bedrooms, all tastefully decorated with en suite facilities, colour TV, hairdryer, shaver point etc. and tea/coffee making facilities. There is a large guest lounge, tea tray on arrival. A real Yorkshire breakfast is served in the dining room.

Places to visit include Castle Howard, Eden Camp, North Yorkshire Moors Railway, Goathland ("Heartbeat"), York etc. There are three pubs, a bistro and a fish and chip shop for meals. Children and dogs welcome. Own keys. Car parking at back of house.

B&B from £30pppn
• SAE please for brochure • Welcome To Excellence
• Hygiene Certificate held • No Smoking
Mrs Ella Bowes

BANAVIE, ROXBY ROAD, THORNTON-LE-DALE, PICKERING YO18 7SX
Tel: 01751 474616
e-mail: info@banavie.uk.com www.banavie.uk.com

Scarborough

SB

Whitby

SB

Situated in the historic town of Whitby, this luxuriously appointed detached residence is on the West Cliff, with sea views yet close to the centre of town. Recently refurbished, this lovely home offers top class accommodation with three en suite bedrooms, two with fabulous sea views and all having hospitality trays, colour TVs and central heating. There is a chiller for the convenience of guests.

Full English breakfasts are served in the lovely dining room, which has separate tables. Parking for three cars. Heather and John offer friendly and personal service to ensure guests are comfortable and content during their stay. Bed and Breakfast from £33 pppn; special rate midweek short breaks available. Non-smoking.

Heather and John Hall • Endeavour B&B
Upgang Lane, Whitby YO21 3EA
Tel: 01947 821110 • e-mail: hhall49@hotmail.com
www.holidayinwhitby.com

Ryedale House   *Established 30 years*   Exclusive to non-smokers, welcoming Yorkshire house of character at the foot of the moors, National Park "Heartbeat" country. Three-and-a-half-miles from Whitby. Magnificent scenery, moors, dales, picturesque harbours, cliffs, beaches, scenic railways, superb walking - it's all here! Highly commended, beautifully appointed rooms with private facilities, many extras. Guest lounge; breakfast room with views over Esk Valley. Enjoy the large south-facing terrace and landscaped gardens. Extensive traditional and vegetarian breakfast choice. Local inns and restaurants - two within a short walk. Parking available, also public transport

SB

Bed and Breakfast: double £30-£32pppn, single £33pppn, minimum stay two nights • Weekly reductions all season. Mid week offers 3-4 nights (not high season) • Regret, no pets or children.

Mrs Pat Beale, Ryedale House, 156 Coach Road, Sleights, Near Whitby YO22 5EQ
Tel & Fax: 01947 810534 • www.ryedalehouse.co.uk

Wi-Fi

York

Alder Carr HOUSE

A country house, set in its own extensive grounds, offering spacious and comfortable accommodation.

- All bedrooms look towards the rolling hills of the Yorkshire Wolds.
- Only a 10 minute drive to York's Park & Ride enables you to combine city sightseeing with quiet country relaxation.
- A wide range of restaurants and country pubs in a three mile radius gives excellent choice for evening meals.
- An ideal base for exploring the many aspects of Yorkshire.
- Twin/double/family rooms - all en suite or private bathroom.
- Price £30-£32.50 per person. Single occupancy in double room £40.

Mr and Mrs G. Steel, Alder Carr House, York Road, Barmby Moor, York YO42 4HT • Tel: 01759 380566 • mobile: 07885 277740
e-mail: chris.steel@aldercarrhouse.plus.com
www.aldercarrhouse.com

oaklands GUEST HOUSE

351 Strensall Road, Earswick,York YO32 9SW

Wi-Fi

A very warm welcome awaits you at our attractive family home set in open countryside, yet only three miles from York. Ideally situated for City, Coast, Dales and Moors.

Our comfortable bedrooms have central heating • en suite facilities • colour TV • razor point • tea & coffee tray • radio alarms • hairdryers

Full breakfast is served in a light airy dining room. Discounts available. Open all year. No pets. Smoking in garden only.

Bed and full English Breakfast from £26.

Telephone: 01904 768443
e-mail: mavmo@oaklands5.fsnet.co.uk

ASCOT HOUSE

80 East Parade, York YO31 7YH
Tel: 01904 426826
Fax: 01904 431077

ETC/AA ★★★★ • ETC SILVER AWARD

An attractive Victorian house with easy access to the historic city centre by walking or by public transport. Many rooms have four-poster or canopy beds, and family and double rooms are en suite. All rooms have central heating, colour TV and tea/coffee facilities. Residential licence. Traditional, Vegetarian and Continental breakfasts. Private enclosed car park.

Singles from £60 to £70, doubles from £70 to £90, Family room from £85 to £115

e-mail: admin@ascothouseyork.com
www.ascothouseyork.com

Blossoms York

Set in a Georgian townhouse on a leafy avenue, a warm welcome awaits at our friendly, family-run guest house. Located only minutes' walk from the historic Bar Walls and York Minster, restaurants, bars and shopping, we are in an ideal location for exploring York. We pride ourselves on offering a good service combined with value-for-money prices. All rooms are recently decorated and en suite with WC and shower; TV, tea tray and phone. Family rooms for up to 6 people. Bar and lounge. Free internet access and wi-fi. Free car park. Local information available.

Sun-Thurs from £22.50pp • Fri and Sat from £30pp
3-night midweek spring and autumn specials from £20pp
See our website for latest prices and offers

Tel: 01904 652391
Fax: 01904 652392
e-mail: fhg@blossomsyork.co.uk

www.blossomsyork.co.uk

Visit the FHG website
www.holidayguides.com
for all kinds of holiday
accommodation in Britain

Doncaster

South Yorkshire

Rock Farm

SB

**Rock Farm, Hooton Pagnell,
Doncaster DN5 7BT
Tel/Fax: 01977 642200
Mobile: 07785 916186
e-mail: info@rockfarm.info
www.rockfarm.info**

A warm welcome and a hearty breakfast await guests at this Grade II
Listed stone farmhouse on a 200-acre mixed farm. Situated in the
picturesque stone-built village of Hooton Pagnell, six miles north-west
of Doncaster, 5 minutes from the A1 and Brodsworth Hall,
10 minutes M62, M1 and M18. Open all year.

Single, double or twin rooms and a twin-bedded suite.

Family rooms from £75, Double rooms from £60
Twin from £50, Single from £28

The FHG Directory of Website Addresses
on pages 390-400 is a useful quick reference guide for
holiday accommodation with e-mail and/or website details

Sheffield

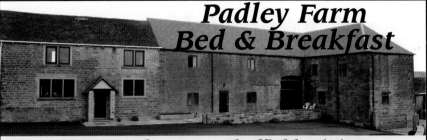
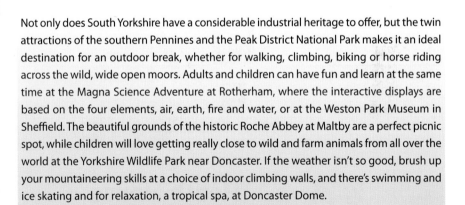
Not only does South Yorkshire have a considerable industrial heritage to offer, but the twin attractions of the southern Pennines and the Peak District National Park makes it an ideal destination for an outdoor break, whether for walking, climbing, biking or horse riding across the wild, wide open moors. Adults and children can have fun and learn at the same time at the Magna Science Adventure at Rotherham, where the interactive displays are based on the four elements, air, earth, fire and water, or at the Weston Park Museum in Sheffield. The beautiful grounds of the historic Roche Abbey at Maltby are a perfect picnic spot, while children will love getting really close to wild and farm animals from all over the world at the Yorkshire Wildlife Park near Doncaster. If the weather isn't so good, brush up your mountaineering skills at a choice of indoor climbing walls, and there's swimming and ice skating and for relaxation, a tropical spa, at Doncaster Dome.

Please note...

West Yorkshire

SB

Wi-Fi

If you are looking for a warm and comfortable environment in which to relax and enjoy your stay whilst visiting Yorkshire then The Manor will be perfect for you. This luxurious 5 Star Gold Award retreat offers a relaxing and refreshing base from which to explore some of the most beautiful countryside in Yorkshire. Lovingly restored, this 18th Century Manor House is enhanced by many original features. Ideally situated for exploring the rugged Pennine moorland or Bronte Country, the Yorkshire Dales and beyond.

- Ample off-road car parking
- Centrally heated en suite rooms
- Welcome tray with homemade biscuits
- Top quality beds and linen
- Satellite TV with DVD player
- Wi-Fi Internet access
- Extensive DVD library
- Hairdryer, CD player & radio alarm clock
- Easy access to all major attractions
- Debit & credit cards accepted
- Private guest lounge
- Thick fluffy towels
- Extensive complimentary toiletries
- Iron & ironing board available
- Packed lunches available on request
- Hearty Yorkshire breakfast menu

The Manor Guest House
Sutton Drive, Cullingworth, Bradford BD13 5BQ
Tel: 01535 274374
e-mail: info@cullingworthmanor.co.uk
www.cullingworthmanor.co.uk

Heath House

An elegant Victorian house set in 4 acres. All en suite rooms are comfortably furnished with TV, tea/coffee tray. Breakfast, which is served in the dining hall, is freshly cooked to order. Wheelchair access to ground floor bedrooms. Children welcome. Well behaved pets welcome. Parking. Open all year. Easy drive to Leeds, Bradford and Dewsbury.

Chancery Road, Ossett, Wakefield WF5 9RZ • 01924 260654
bookings@heath-house.co.uk • www.heath-house.co.uk

West Yorkshire is a mix of wild moorland and towns and cities with an historic industrial heritage. Spend some time in one of the many fascinating museums of past working life, then stride out over the moors, taking in the dramatic scenery, before a shopping spree or a wonderful afternoon tea. Visit the Rhubarb Triangle near Wakefield early in the year to see the crop being harvested by candlelight. At the model Victorian village for mill workers at Saltaire UNESCO World Heritage Site, Salts Mill has been transformed into the Hockney Gallery, with a restaurant and everything from musical instruments to carpets for shoppers to browse and buy. From there, wander along the banks of the Leeds-Liverpool Canal, so vital for trade in a past age, and watch the Five Rise Locks in action. Leeds is the destination for a lively city break. Theatres, ballet, opera, festivals, restaurants, clubs, and of course, one of the best shopping experiences in the country, all are here to provide entertainment and a memorable stay. Visit the exclusive shops in the Victoria Quarter and find sought after brands in the new developments at The Light and Clarence Dock on the waterside. If all this is too much for some family members, Harewood House with its wonderful interior, gardens, and adventure playground is nearby, as well as the Yorkshire Planetarium.

Durham

If you're looking for a few days' break somewhere different, why not go to the city of Durham? Set between the North Pennines and the Durham Heritage Coast, the old medieval heart with its cobbled streets is dominated by the cathedral and castle, a World Heritage Site, and a must for visitors. On the way back to the modern shopping centre, browse through individual boutiques and galleries in the alleys and vennels, and the stalls of the Victorian market, then enjoy a stroll along the riverside walks. Stay for longer in County Durham, tour all the heritage sites and enjoy invigorating walks and hikes through the dramatic Pennines countryside and along the clifftop path at the coast. There are paths, trails and tracks for all standards of fitness, whether a family ramble and picnic or a hike along the Pennine Way. High Force, the highest waterfall in England, on the Raby Castle estate, is easily accessible.

Spennymoor

Northumberland

Rambling over the heather-clad Cheviot moorlands, exploring the castles and pele towers
built to ward off invading Scots, watching the feast of wildlife on the coast and in the
countryside, breathing in the wonderful sea air on a golden sandy beach, you'll find it all
in Northumberland. On the coast, a designated Area of Outstanding Natural Beauty, keen
walkers can take the Coast Path from the walled Georgian market town of Berwick-on-
Tweed to Cresswell, stopping at little fishing villages on the way. Follow the section along
Embleton beach from Craster, best known for its traditionally smoked kippers, to get the
best views of the ruins of Dunstanburgh Castle. At the lively market town of Alnwick visit
the castle, Hogwarts in the Harry Potter films, with its redeveloped gardens, magnificent
water features and even a poison garden!

Alnmouth

SB

Wi-Fi

Alnmouth - Westlea

Janice invites you to stay in her spacious home situated by the water's edge of the beautiful Aln Estuary, combining superior accommodation with superb value.

- Fabulous panoramic views of the beautiful Aln Estuary and surrounding countryside can be enjoyed from the balconies of our first floor bedroom, guest lounge and from our dining room.

- All bedrooms are en suite, with hospitality trays, colour TV, hairdryers, alarm clock radios, centrally heated and have been recently refurbished to a very high standard – some with Tester and Crown drapes and balconies.

- Three bedrooms are ground floor. We have a wide front door and wheelchair ramp.

- A large choice of breakfasts includes: Continental, healthy options as well as full hearty English breakfasts.

- EVENING MEALS are served at Westlea. Janice and her chef Paul are renowned for their traditional and imaginative gourmet cuisine, using fresh local produce and glorious desserts to spoil you.

- Private parking • Prices vary according to rooms.

- **Winner of numerous hospitality awards**
- **Most popular hotel/guest house awards**
- **Overall Contribution to Tourism Award**
- **Galloping Gourmet Award**
- **Winter Warmer Gourmet Breaks available**

" Food exceptional in terms of quality and flair and variety of culinary delights"
(A happy visitor)

" Beautiful home with outstanding views and most friendly and helpful staff. Excellent in every way"
(A previous visitor)

Mrs Janice Edwards, Alnmouth-Westlea
29 Riverside Road, Alnmouth, Northumberland NE66 2SD
Tel: 01665 830730
e-mail: westlea.alnmouth@hotmail.com

The guest house visitors return to year after year

SB

SB
Wi-Fi

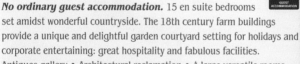

Rare and endangered wildlife is found all along the coast and the ultimate destination for enthusiasts is the Farne Islands, with boat trips from the family resort of Seahouses to watch the grey seals and seabirds, including puffins, in the breeding seasons. Wildlife is abundant in the uplands to the west too. In the heather moorlands of the Cheviot Hills there are plenty of opportunities for birdwatching, as well as horse riding, fishing, canoeing and rock climbing, while at Kielder Water and Forest Park watch the red squirrels and ospreys, follow forest trails and mountain bike tracks or watch the stars in the dark night skies. Learn too about the Romans by watching a re-enactment of Roman life at one of the settlements along Hadrian's Wall, or walk along its length from coast to coast.

The Rob Roy

**Dock Road, Tweedmouth
Berwick-upon-Tweed
Northumberland TD15 2BE
Tel & Fax: 01289 306428**

Your hosts Ian and Linda Woods extend to you the warmest welcome to this family-run Northumberland B&B.

Situated in Tweedmouth, in historic Berwick-upon-Tweed, the Rob Roy is a guest house in the classic, welcoming Northumberland style.

Within easy walking distance of Berwick-upon-Tweed town centre and also Spittal beach and promenade.

Perfect for Northumberland holidays and visitors keen to explore the open country, historic sites and remarkable coastline of this beautiful county.

The five bedrooms, three double rooms, one twin room, and a family room, all have en suite facilities and are comfortable and stylishly furnished with television, tea and coffee making facilities, alarm clocks and hairdryers. Free Wi-Fi is also available.

The guest lounge with real fire and stone walls is the perfect place to relax and can also be used for a private function or business meeting.

The fully licensed bar is well stocked with real ales and a selection of wines, while the popular beer garden is a great way to enjoy a drink whilst taking in the views of the River Tweed as it joins the North Sea.

Prices start from £60 per night for a double or twin room, £75 for the family room and £45 for single occupancy.

Prices include breakfast, chosen from a full English selection or alternatives. Lunches and dinners are also available at the Rob Roy in our Harbour Lights Restaurant, serving the best of fresh produce locally sourced wherever possible.

www.robroyberwick.co.uk • e-mail: therobroy@hotmail.co.uk

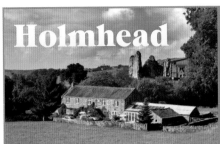

Bush Nook Guest House
Hadrian's Wall Country

Experience the wildness, freshness, culture and two millennia of history

Bush Nook Guest House is a traditional farmhouse situated within the wonderful Hadrian's Wall countryside, with panoramic views east to Northumberland National Park and Kielder Forest.

Comfortably furnished 4 star Bed and Breakfast accommodation, all bedrooms en suite, most with open beamed ceilings.

The area has excellent walking and cycling routes, offering open countryside, peacefulness, and fresh air. Easily accessible from both east and west.

Also available: superbly equipped 4 star self-catering holiday cottage in the Hay Barn, sleeping two people, with exceptional space and atmosphere. Sofa bed for an additional two people, ideal for a group or family unit for a cost effective holiday break.

Rooms rates including breakfast from £35pppn
Special Breaks available – see website for details.
Quote FHG12 to receive 5% discount

Bush Nook, Upper Denton, Gilsland CA8 7AF
Tel: 01697 747194 • info@bushnook.co.uk
www.bushnook.co.uk

THE Bay Horse INN
NORTHUMBERLAND

West Woodburn, Hexham NE48 2RX

The Bay Horse Inn, West Woodburn, is a delightful 18th century coaching inn built in mellow sandstone, nestling by a stone bridge over the River Rede in the Cheviot Hills of Northumberland, the perfect base for many outdoor pursuits and activities. This is the place to stop on your journey: to rest, drink, eat well and relax in a warm friendly, informal atmosphere.

Excellent home-cooked cuisine is popular with locals and visitors alike.

Comfortable accommodation is available in 7 en suite bedrooms, all individually decorated in a delightful cottage style, with TV, tea and coffee making facilities, hairdryer, ironing facilities and a trouser press.

On the A68, 6 miles from Otterburn, 20 miles from Corbridge, 24 miles from Newcastle Airport; ideally placed for Hadrian's Wall, Kielder Water, Alnwick and the Scottish Borders.

Tel: 01434 270218
enquiry@bayhorseinn.org
www.bayhorseinn.org

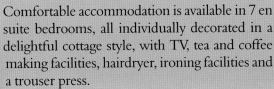

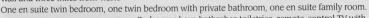
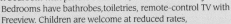

The Anglers Arms

A Legend in the very Heart of Northumberland

This traditional Coaching Inn is situated only 6 miles from Morpeth, beside picturesque Weldon Bridge on the River Coquet.

Accommodation at the Anglers Arms consists of two cosy en suite bedrooms, one double and one twin, and a generously proportioned self contained flat on the upper floor, with double bedroom, large living room and luxury bathroom. Bedrooms are cosy and welcoming, with a touch of olde worlde charm.

Be prepared for a hearty Northumbrian breakfast! Meals can be be enjoyed in the friendly bar, or outdoors on sunny summer days; alternatively dine in style and sophistication in the à la carte Pullman Railway Carriage restaurant. Ideal for exploring both coast and country, the Inn also caters for fishermen, with its own one-mile stretch of the River Coquet available free to residents.

The Anglers Arms

Weldon Bridge, Longframlington, Northumberland NE65 8AX

Tel: 01665 570271/570655

info@anglersarms.fsnet.co.uk • www.anglersarms.com

SB

Wi-Fi

SB
♀

Wi-Fi

Cheshire

Jo and Pete Hollins offer guests a friendly welcome to their home on a 145-acre working farm in quiet and peaceful surroundings. Green Farm is situated on the Cheshire/Staffordshire border and is within easy reach of Junction 16 on the M6. An excellent stop-over place for travellers journeying between north and south of the country.

Two family rooms en suite; two double and two twin en suite in converted cottage can be either B&B or self-catering using the fully equipped kitchen in the cottage; all on ground floor. Tea-making facilities and TV in all rooms. Cot provided.

Bed and Breakfast from £25 per person.

Open all year • Caravans and tents welcome

This area offers many attractions; we are within easy reach of historic Chester, Alton Towers and the famous Potteries of Staffordshire.

01270 820214

Balterley Green Farm, Deans Lane, Balterley, Near Crewe CW2 5QJ
www.bedandbreakfast-cheshire.co.uk

WHITE WALLS a 100 year old converted stables, in the heart of award-winning village of Christleton, two miles from Chester, off the A41, close to A55, M53 and North Wales. Walking distance to village pub and two canalside pub/restaurants, church, village shop, hairdresser and bus stop. Half-hourly bus service to Chester. The village pond is home to swans, mallards, Aylesbury ducks and moorhens. En suite double bedroom, twin-bedded room with washbasin, all including English Breakfast. Minimum rates from £35 single, £50 double. Colour TV, tea/coffee making facilities, central heating, overlooking garden. Non-smoking. Not suitable for children or pets. Free Wi-Fi.

SB

Wi-Fi

Brian and Hilary Devenport, White Walls,
Village Road, Christleton, Chester CH3 7AS
Tel: 01244 336033 • e-mail: hilary-devenport@supanet.com

The Plough at Eaton

Macclesfield Road, Eaton,
Near Congleton, Cheshire CW12 2NH
Tel: 01260 280207 • Fax: 01260 298377
e-mail: theploughinn@hotmail.co.uk • www.plough-eaton.co.uk

AA
★★★★
INN

Traditional oak beams and blazing log fires in winter reflect the warm and friendly atmosphere of this half-timbered former coaching inn which dates from the 17th century. The heart of the 'Plough' is the kitchen where food skilfully prepared is calculated to satisfy the most discerning palate. Luncheons and dinners are served seven days a week with traditional roasts on Sundays. In peaceful, rolling countryside near the Cheshire/Staffordshire border, this is a tranquil place in which to stay and the hostelry has elegantly colour-co-ordinated guest rooms, all with spacious bathrooms, LCD colour television, direct-dial telephone and tea and coffee-making facilities amongst their impressive appointments. Wireless internet access available.

Chester

Alston, Ambleside

Cumbria

Ambleside

Ambleside

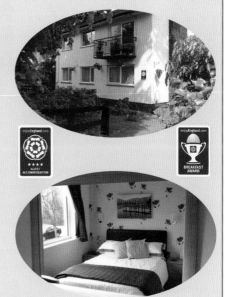

Ambleside

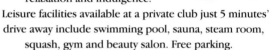
SB

Ambleside

Carlisle

Carlisle, Cockermouth

The stunning scenery of the region now known as Cumbria, in England's north west, from the Solway Firth in the north to the coasts of Morecambe Bay in the south, the ports and seaside villages in the west to the Pennines in the east, and including the Lake District National Park, has been attracting tourists since the end of the 17th century, and the number of visitors has been increasing ever since. All kinds of outdoor activities are available, from gorge walking and ghyll scrambling to a trek through the countryside on horseback or a quiet afternoon rowing on a tranquil lake. The area is a walkers' paradise, and whether on foot, in a wheelchair or a pushchair there's a path and trail for everyone.

Keswick

Keswick

SB

Bassenthwaite Hall Farm B&B

A friendly welcome awaits you at our lovely 17thC farmhouse which is fully modernised whilst retaining its olde worlde character. A charming lounge/dining room furnished with antiques is available for guests' use any time. The delightful bedrooms have individual period furnishings and washbasins; two bathrooms nearby; annexed en suite rooms also available. Tea and coffee making facilities available. An excellent Cumbrian Breakfast starts the day, or choose a lighter option.

Single from £38 per night, Twin/Double from £30pppn, Family Room from £75 per night.

Our farmhouse is by the stream and a wooden footbridge where ducks swim happily all day. A gentle stroll further up the riverside takes you to the 17th Century village inn where good food is served.

Bassenthwaite Hall Farm, Bassenthwaite Village, Near Keswick, Cumbria CA12 4QP

Tel: **01768 776393**• **www.bedandbreakfast-lakedistrict.co.uk**
e-mail: **info@loftholidaycottages.co.uk**

SB

Wi-Fi

ROOMS36 • Keswick

Rooms36 is a Bed and Breakfast located in the beautiful market town of Keswick in the heart of the Lake District. We are situated only 2 minutes flat walk from Keswick town centre and Derwentwater, "Queen of the Lakes", with its fine views and water activities.

All bedrooms have en suite facilities, colour TV, hospitality tray and central heating.

Full English breakfast consists of locally sourced, fresh, free-range produce. We cater for all diets.

Andy & Charlotte will do their best to make your stay an extremely comfortable and enjoyable one. Two nights minimum stay • Rooms36 B&B is dog friendly • Open over Christmas and New Year.

36 Lake Road, Keswick, Cumbria CA12 5DQ
Tel: **017687 72764** • Freephone: **0800 056 6401**
Mobile: **07721 957899**

andy@rooms36.co.uk • **www.rooms36.co.uk**

Keswick

Keswick

Kirkby Stephen, Kirksanton

SB

Wi-Fi

SB

Penrith, Ravenstonedale, Ullswater

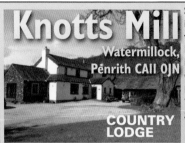

Windermere

Windermere

Windermere

St John's Lodge

Lake Road, Windermere,
Cumbria LA23 2EQ
Tel: 015394 43078 • Fax: 015394 88054
e-mail: mail@st-johns-lodge.co.uk
www.st-johns-lodge.co.uk

This pretty Lakeland B&B is ideally situated between Windermere village and the lake (10 minutes' walk) and close to all amenities. The guesthouse caters exclusively for non-smokers and has been awarded 3 AA Stars, Highly Commended.

The choice of breakfast menu is probably the largest in the area. From a touring visitor's point of view, or if you prefer healthier alternatives, this is a refreshing change. There is the usual choice of cereals and fresh fruit and a good selection of traditional English breakfasts, but there are also over 20 other tasty dishes, including vegetarian/vegan/gluten free, fresh fish, and a number of house specialities.

Free Wi-Fi is available.

On a working farm, lovely, spacious farmhouse dating from the 16th century, with beams and old oak panelling in guest lounge. The poet, William Wordsworth, used to visit here. Magnificent scenery. Conveniently situated approximately 4 miles from Lake Windermere, one mile from the B5284 main road. 30 minutes from Junction 36 M6. Handy for Beatrix Potter attractions.

Bed and Breakfast £35pppn.

Two double and one triple/twin en suite rooms with TV, hospitality tray, hairdryer.
TV lounge/breakfast room • No smoking • No pets • Open February to December.
'Bed & Breakfast Nationwide' Inspected & Approved.

**Mrs Pat Metcalfe, Crook Hall Farm B&B,
Crook, Near Kendal, Cumbria LA8 8LF
Tel: 01539 821352
e-mail: metcalfe@crookhallfarm.co.uk
www.crookhallfarm.co.uk**

Blackpool

Lancashire

Generations of excited holiday-makers have visited Lancashire's coastal resorts, and amongst them Blackpool stands out as the star attraction. For seaside fun, amusements and entertainment it's difficult to beat, but the quieter resorts along the coast with traditional seaside attractions have their own appeal. For an outdoor break there are all kinds of activities from hot air ballooning to fishing on offer inland, from the lowland plain, along the winding valleys of the Ribble and the Lune, up into the Forest of Bowland and on to the moors of the western Pennines. Further north at Morecambe take part in the Catch the Wind Kite Festival held on the sands in July, just one of a number of events in the town each year. With the winds blowing in every direction conditions on this Irish Sea coast are perfect for kite-surfing, and instruction is available at Fleetwood, a family-orientated Victorian resort where the Fylde Folk Festival is held every September.

A large detached bungalow, three miles south of Lancaster and 400 yards from Lancaster University. Access from M6 Junction 33 and A6.

Two double bedrooms each with shower, toilet, colour TV and tea/coffee making facilities. One bedroom also has a private TV lounge. Full central heating. Spacious parking. A good location for visiting Blackpool, Morecambe, the Lake District and Yorkshire Dales. You will be sure of a friendly welcome and a homely atmosphere.

Bed and Breakfast from £25 per person • Sorry, no pets
Non-smokers only please • Open all year

Roy and Helen Domville, Three Gables, Chapel Lane, Galgate, Lancaster LA2 0PN • 01524 752222

Anglesey

Anglesey & Gwynedd

SB

Wi-Fi

Ingledene

A large Edwardian seaside home with magnificent views across Trearddur Bay provides a warm and friendly welcome for your stay.

Spacious twin/double rooms (three en suite), most with sea views. Relax and watch the glorious sunsets and wake up to the sound of the waves.

All rooms are centrally heated with Freeview TV and tea/coffee making facilities. Wireless internet is available.

Parking at rear with ample space for boats, canoes, etc.

Holyhead ferry terminal is only 10 minutes away with day trips to Ireland available. The Anglesey Coastal Path goes past the door.

Bed and Breakfast from £30 per person (Single £40). Open all year. Self-catering cottage (sleeps 2+2) also available.

Richard and Shirley Murphy, Ingledene,
Ravenspoint Road, Trearddur Bay LL65 2YU
Tel: 01407 861026
e-mail: info@ingledene.co.uk
www.ingledene.co.uk

Mountains, rivers, lakes, cliffs, estuaries and sea attract tourists searching for all different kinds of break to Anglesey & Gwynedd. Families love the unspoilt beaches and extensive sands, the quiet seaside villages like Aberdaron, Victorian Criccieth or busier Barmouth with traditional seaside fun. For a more active holiday, at Aberdyfi, a popular resort with a thriving little harbour, you'll find all kinds of watersports, including sailing, sailboarding, fishing and boat trips, and there is also an 18-hole championship golf course. The Llyn Peninsula also boasts some of the best sailing and surfing beaches in North Wales and its capital, Pwllheli, has an impressive marina which berths over 400 boats and has space for overnight mooring.

Time, space and freedom to explore beautiful
NORTH WALES

Minutes from the stunning mountains of Snowdonia and the glorious beaches of Anglesey, North Wales offers an experience unlike any other. Historical landscapes, mythical legends, arts and crafts as well as a taste of the modern; the space to explore them all is in abundance.

Let the dramatic scenery inspire you while our facilities at Bangor University impress you. With a dedicated team of staff on hand throughout your stay, we have everything you need to ensure your time with us is memorable.

So whether you're a group of 3 or a company of 300, if you're looking for an inspirational location, nature's own adventure playground, or a place to rest your head between activities in North Wales, then join us at Bangor.

We offer :

Catered Individual & Group Accommodation

Conference & Banqueting

Fine Dining

Corporate meeting space

Social Functions

Christmas Parties

Executive Boardroom Hire

Individually tailored packages

On site Leisure Facilities

Tel: 01248 388088   conferences@bangor.ac.uk

www.bangor.ac.uk/conferences

Conwy, Criccieth

Dulas Bay, Harlech

Beautiful Victorian Country House standing in 23 acres of woodland, gardens and fields.
High standard of accommodation in family, twin and double rooms, all en suite.

Guest lounge and dining room with panoramic view of Dulas Bay. Extensive garden with woodland walks.

Traditional Welsh breakfast with produce from own 'True Taste of Wales' Award-Winning Smokery.

Children welcome.

Pets welcome. Stabling/grazing available.
Mrs Gwen McCreadie

Deri Isaf

Dulas Bay, Isle of Anglesey LL70 9DX
Tel: 01248 410536 • Mobile: 07721 374471
e-mail: mccreadie@deriisaf.freeserve.co.uk
www.angleseyfarms.com/deri.htm

 Cymru Wales ★★★★

 SILVER ARIAN 2009 ANGLESEY TOURISM AWARDS GWOBRAU TWRISTIAETH MÔN

 WINNER ENILLYDD 2010 TOURISM AWARDS GWOBRAU TWRISTIAETH MÔN

Best Bed & Breakfast/Guesthouse

SB

Hotel Maes-y-Neuadd

Talsarnau, Near Harlech LL47 6YA
Tel: 01766 780200
Fax: 01766 780211
e-mail: maes@neuadd.com
www.neuadd.com

A warm welcome awaits you at this historic Welsh manor house, nestled on a hillside in the heart of Snowdonia, with fabulous views of the mountains and coast. Dating back to 14th century, this beautiful granite building is now a 4-Star Gold Award country house hotel, set amongst 80 acres of gardens, parkland, forest and vegetable/kitchen gardens. Happily, 21st century amenities together with excellent friendly service ensure a relaxing and comfortable stay! Ideally situated for exploring Snowdonia and its many attractions and with a range of rooms and prices to suit all tastes and budgets; an award-winning restaurant serving fresh local produce (much from our own gardens) and an excellent wine list – it's definitely a great place to stay and well worth paying us a visit!

We are open for morning coffee, lunch, afternoon tea, dinner or, if you fancy a treat, champagne and strawberries on the terrace!

Children welcome – children's menu, early teas, baby listening, family dining room.
Dogs also welcome in two of our Coach House rooms – dog sitting by arrangement.

Good Hotel Guide
Country House Hotel
of the Year 2003

 Cymru Wales ★★★★

 Cymru Wales Gwobr *Aur* Gold Award 2009/2010

symbols ⋔⚘SB♿♉Wi-Fi

⋔	Pets Welcome	⚘	Children Welcome
SB	Short Breaks	♿	Suitable for Disabled Guests
♉	Licensed	Wi-Fi	Wi-Fi available

Tywyn

SB

Eisteddfa offers you the comfort of a
newly-built bungalow on the Tan-y-coed
Ucha Farm, situated adjacent to the
farmhouse but with all the benefits of
Bed and Breakfast accommodation.
The bungalow, which has been designed
to accommodate disabled guests,
is conveniently situated between Abergynolwyn and Dolgoch Falls with Talyllyn Narrow
Gauge Railway running through the farmland. Three bedrooms, two en suite and the third
with a shower and washbasin suitable for a disabled person. The toilet is located in the
adjacent bathroom. Tea/coffee tray and TV are provided in the bedrooms as are many other
extras. We also cater for Coeliac Diets.

Cymru
Wales
★★★★

Abergynolwyn, Tywyn LL36 9UP
Mrs Gweniona Pugh • 01654 782385
e-mail: hugh.pugh01@btinternet.com

AA
★★★★
FARMHOUSE

North Wales

Betws-y-Coed

SB

Bron Celyn Guest House, Lôn Muriau, Llanrwst Road,
Betws-y-Coed LL24 0HD • Tel: 01690 710333 • Fax: 01690 710111

A warm welcome awaits you at this delightful guest house overlooking the
Gwydyr Forest and Llugwy/Conwy Valleys and village of Betws-y-Coed in
Snowdonia National Park. Ideal centre for touring, walking, climbing, fishing
and golf. Also excellent overnight stop en route for Holyhead ferries.
Easy walk into village and close to Conwy/Swallow Falls and Fairy Glen.
Most rooms en suite, all with colour TV and beverage makers. Lounge.
Full central heating. Garden. Car park. Open all year. Full hearty breakfast, packed
meals, evening meals - special diets catered for. Walkers and Cyclists Welcome.
B&B from £24 to £35, reduced rates for children under 12 years.
Special out of season breaks.
Jim and Lilian Boughton
e-mail: welcome@broncelyn.co.uk • www.broncelyn.co.uk

Cymru
Wales
★★★

Vine House Bed & Breakfast

23 Church Walks, Llandudno LL30 2HG
Tel: 01492 876493
www.vinehouse-llandudno.co.uk

Will and Margaret welcome you to Vine House, their friendly family-run Guest House situated just across the road from the famous Great Orme Victorian Tramway.

We offer comfortable accommodation in two en suite double rooms, one en suite triple/family room,and one en suite twin/superking double. You will have a sea view or a view of the Great Orme from whichever room you stay in, and all rooms have digital TV, tea/coffee tray and hairdryer. Iron and ironing board are available for your use - please ask.

You are welcome to use the front garden to take your afternoon tea or while away those long sunny summer evenings! Full cooked breakfast or lighter options served. We are happy to take children (discounts up to age 16) and dogs by arrangement (a small charge applies)

There is no smoking allowed anywhere in the house but you are welcome to use the front garden if you wish.

Carmarthenshire

Carmarthenshire is one of the best regions for an activity or leisure break, with everything from mountain biking in the Brechfa Forest to canoeing and kayaking in the challenging stretches of the Teifi river, from walking in the foothills of the Brecon Beacons to a quiet day's fishing for sewin, salmon or trout in some remote river. There are championship courses for golfers, as well as a wide choice offering affordable golf to players of all abilities, and a chance of a day's horse racing at the new venue at Ffos Las. The Millennium Coastal Park is one of the most popular tourist attractions in Britain, with breathtaking views of the Gower Peninsula, and a unique variety of attractions stretching from Pembrey Country Park with its acres of beautiful parkland, and one of the best beaches in the UK, as well as many excellent family activities.

SB

Wi-Fi

Plas Farm B&B · Llangynog, Carmarthen

PLAS FARM B&B, run by the Thomas family for the past 100 years, offers guests peaceful accommodation on a family-run dairy farm, in a quiet location, ideal as a touring base. Very spacious, comfortable farmhouse with colour TV and welcome tray in all bedrooms. All rooms en suite or with private shower room. TV lounge. Full central heating. Evening meals available at local country inn nearby. Warm welcome assured.

En route to Fishguard and Pembroke Ferries. Ample safe parking. Good golf course minutes away.

B&B from £27.50 per person.
Children under 16 years sharing
family room half price.
A warm welcome awaits.
"Welcome Host"
Mrs Margaret Thomas, Plas Farm,
Llangynog, Carmarthen SA33 5DB
Tel: 01267 211492
mobile: 07530 644278
www.plasfarmbedandbreakfast.co.uk
e-mail: plasfarm@hotmail.co.uk

Best Western Diplomat Hotel
Felinfoel, Llanelli SA15 3PJ
Tel: 01554 756156 • Fax: 01554 751649
AA/WTB ★★★

The Diplomat Hotel offers a rare combination of charm and character, with excellent well appointed facilities to ensure your comfort. Explore the Gower Peninsula and the breathtaking West Wales coastline.
Salmon & trout fishing, horse riding, golf, and motor racing at Pembrey are all within reach.

e-mail: reservations@diplomat-hotel-wales.com • www.bw-diplomathotel.co.uk

All our 50 bedrooms are stylish and modern, boasting much character and charm. Modern luxury and comfort is integrated with traditional furnishings, allowing relaxation with the familiar comforts of home.
All of our rooms include the following:
En-suite facilities • Direct-dial telephone
Television • Tea & coffee-making facilities
Hairdryer • High speed internet access
Use of Chasens Health Club and Spa

Our chefs use the finest, freshest ingredients, sourced locally where ever possible, with imaginative presentation to excite the palate. Recently added to the front of the historic mansion, the Atrium is a wonderful fully glassed conservatory, which is comfortably air-conditioned. During the summer, drinks can be enjoyed on the terrace outside the conservatory. We are open to non-residents for morning coffee, lunch, afternoon teas and dinner.

Ceredigion

PENBONTBREN

Cymru Wales ★★★★★
Cymru Wales Star Gold award

Luxury Bed and Breakfast in West Wales

Penbontbren
Glynarthen, Llandysul, Near Cardigan
Ceredigion SA44 6PE
Tel: 01239 810248
email: contact@penbontbren.com
www.penbontbren.com

SB

Wi-Fi

Penbontbren Luxury Bed and Breakfast in West Wales is nestled in 32 acres of grounds, surrounded by beautiful countryside with views towards the Preseli mountains, and is only 2 miles from wonderful National Trust beaches. 5 luxury suites are equipped to a 5 star standard, each with spacious sitting room, own garden, king-size bed and sumptuous décor and furnishings. Substantial Welsh breakfasts are prepared from locally sourced ingredients. Pets are welcome by prior arrangement. Luxury self-catering cottage also available.

Come to Ceredigion for spectacular scenery, from the cliffs and golden beaches of the coast to the uplands of the Cambrian Mountains, only some half an hour's drive the sea. This rural county, a centre for Welsh language and culture, is home to the National Library of Wales at Aberystwyth, but the books and manuscripts held there aren't the only attraction for visitors. For an active holiday break there are activity centres for all age groups, sea angling and shore fishing, walking in the mountains and along the coast, challenging mountain bike trails and quiet roads for cycling and all kinds of golf courses from parkland to coastal links. Boat trips take visitors out dolphin-spotting, and many species of bird are to be seen along the coast, including Red Kite. Tresaith, one of the locations most favoured by visitors to Ceredigion, is an almost picture-book seaside village with a wonderful sandy beach, ideal for families, with clean sands, clear waters, and rocks to climb, whilst inland lies the Teifi Valley - offering marvellous angling - and Cenarth's famous falls.

Please note...

Haverfordwest

Pembrokeshire

Pembrokeshire's entire coastline is a designated National Park, with sheltered coves and wooded estuaries, a wide choice of award-winning sandy beaches and some of the most dramatic cliffs in Britain. The islands of Skomer, Stokholm and Grasholm are home to thousands of seabirds, and cruise round Skomer is a great opportunity to watch the puffins. Ramsey Island, as well as being an RSPB Reserve boasts the second largest grey seal colony in Britain. You can watch them on a seal safari, or take a boat trip to go whale and dolphin spotting off the coast. Enjoy the wonderful views from the clifftop golf courses, or while walking round the Pembrokeshire Coastal Path. Conditions are ideal for all kinds of water sports including surfing, scuba diving and windsurfing, or try coasteering, a combination of climbing, swimming and leaping round the rocky coast.

Ivybridge

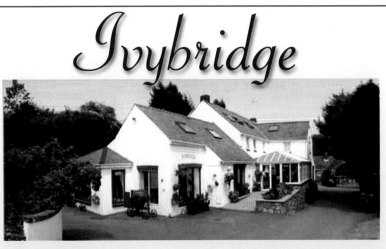

Welcome to Ivybridge

Situated in a quiet part of Goodwick, Ivybridge is a friendly, family-run guest house offering comfortable accommodation just outside of Fishguard, a picturesque area of Pembrokeshire, within easy reach of the Pembrokeshire coastal paths, the historic City of St David's and beautiful beaches.

Try our small heated indoor swimming pool, relax in our conservatory or put your feet up in front of a roaring fire in the bar/lounge area and enjoy the company and atmosphere at Ivybridge.

All rooms are en suite, with Freeview television, hairdryers and hot drink facilities. Wake up to a Full Welsh Breakfast or a Continental Breakfast. Vegetarian guests are welcome and all dietary needs can be catered for. At Ivybridge we offer home cooked evening meals by arrangement using fresh locally sourced ingredients wherever possible (please book before arrival). We serve evening meals between 6.30-7.30 pm. Our guests are more than welcome to bring friends and family to dine with them. We also cater for smaller functions and parties.

For further information
please contact us
Ivybridge, Drim Mill, Dyffryn,
Goodwick SA64 0JT
Tel: 01348 875366 • Fax: 01348 872338
e-mail: ivybridge5366@aol.com
www.ivybridgeleisure.co.uk

Cymru
Wales
★★★

Powys

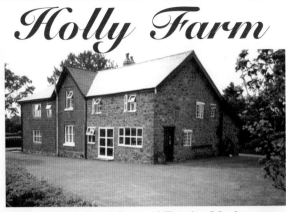

Newtown

SB

The Forest
COUNTRY HOUSE B&B

Cymru Wales
★★★★★

Hidden in the beautiful Vale of Kerry,
The Forest offers 5-star luxury bed and breakfast in
five charming en suite rooms (one with four-poster).
All bedrooms have flat screen satellite TV, DVD
player, telephone and tea tray; free Wi-Fi internet
available in all rooms. Guests can relax in the
spacious drawing room and dining room, and enjoy
the four acres of gardens, tennis court, and games
room. Kennels and stables are available.
This secluded and peaceful location is perfect to
explore the many attractions of Mid-Wales.
Self catering cottages available.

**Paul & Michelle Martin, The Forest, Gilfach Lane,
Kerry, Newtown, Powys SY16 4DW
Tel: 01686 621 821
e-mail: info@theforestkerry.co.uk
www.bedandbreakfastnewtown.co.uk**

SB

Greenfields
Bed & Breakfast

Cymru Wales
★★★

A warm welcome awaits you at Greenfields
All rooms are tastefully decorated and are spacious in size, each having
panoramic views of the rolling Kerry hills. There is a good choice of breakfast
menu, and packed lunches are also available; the dining room has individual
tables. Accommodation available in twin, double, family and single rooms,
all en suite (twin rooms let as singles if required). Hostess tray and TV in
all rooms. A good place for stopping for one night, a short break or longer
holiday. Excellent off-road parking. Brochure available.
**B&B from £52 double or twin room, from £26 single
and £75 family room.**

**Mrs Vi Madeley, Greenfields,
Kerry, Newtown, Powys SY16 4LH
Tel: 01686 670596
Mobile: 07971 075687 • Fax: 01686 670354
e-mail: info@greenfields-bb.co.uk
www.greenfields-bb.co.uk**

Welshpool

Lane Farm

*A **warm welcome awaits*** on our working organic beef and sheep farm situated between Welshpool and Shrewsbury. Nestling beneath the tranquil Breidden Hills in the picturesque Severn Valley, ideally situated to explore The Marches, Shropshire Hills and Mid Wales. Accommodation consists of four spacious, modern, en suite bedrooms, two on the ground floor. All rooms have central heating, TV, beverage tray and radio alarm clock. Guests' sitting room. Hearty farmhouse breakfasts. Local pubs offering excellent evening meals just a short drive or walk away.

Ample safe parking • Free fishing by arrangement .

**Tel: 01743 884288 • Lane Farm, Criggion, Near Welshpool, Powys SY5 9BG
e-mail: lesley@lanefarmbedandbreakfast.co.uk
www.lanefarmbedandbreakfast.com**

Powys is situated right on England's doorstep and boasts some of most spectacular scenery in Europe. It is ideal for an action-packed holiday with fishing, golf, pony trekking, climbing caving and canoeing readily available, and walkers have a choice of everything from riverside trails to mountain hikes, including The Beacons Way, crossing the beautiful Brecon Beacons National Park, the Offa's Dyke Path running for 177 miles through Border country, often following the ancient earthworks, and Glyndwr's Way which takes in some of the finest landscape features in Wales. At Machynlleth take a ride on the amazing water-balanced cliff railway at the Centre for Alternative Technology, visit the border towns with their Georgian architecture and half-timbered black and white houses to visit, or wander round the wonderful shops in the book town of Hay, famous for its Literary Festival each May. In fact every year there are festivals and events throughout the region, from the World Bog Snorkelling Championships at Llanwrtyd Wells to local fairs and galas.

Pubs & Inns

See the Supplement on pages 373-378

South Wales

Neath

Green Lanterns

18th Century luxury Guest House where our aim is to ensure a peaceful, comfortable and relaxing stay. Our guest rooms are all en suite and spacious, and have central heating, colour TV, tea and coffee making facilities, and panoramic views over the Vale of Neath.

Licensed bar and restaurant • Vegetarian & other diets catered for
Children welcome • Parking • Non-smoking rooms
• Major credit cards accepted • Pets welcome by arrangement
www.greenlanterns.co.uk

Mrs C. Jones
Green Lanterns Guest House
Hawdref Ganol Farm, Cimla, Neath SA12 9SL
01639 631884 • WTB ★★★★

As well as being an ideal holiday destination in its own right Swansea Bay is a perfect base for touring the rest of South Wales. Just a short journey from the city you will find the seaside village of Mumbles and the Gower Peninsula. A great place for all sorts of watersports such as sailing and kite surfing, the beaches are perfect for surfing, for beginners and experts alike. Cycle along one of the traffic-free routes or use up extra energy on the challenging mountain bike tracks of the Afan Forest Park. To the east follow the coastal path along the beautiful Glamorgan Heritage Coast, for views of the dramatic cliffs and the network of sand dunes at Merthyr Mawr, and golfers will enjoy a round at one of the many golf courses here, including the famous Royal Porthcawl. For something different visit the Wye Valley and the Vale of Usk with awesome castles, breathtaking scenery and a rich and colourful history. The area is steeped in industrial heritage, and at Blaenavon World Heritage Site visitors can go underground with a miner and uncover real stories about people from the past. Many staff at Rhondda Heritage Park claim to have seen a phantom miner, or the ghost of a woman with two young children, and the legendary King Arthur is also reputed to have connections to the valleys. Cardiff is one of the UK's top shopping venues, with modern shopping malls, Edwardian and Victorian arcades and a weekly farmers' market, as well as independent chain stores and boutiques. The architecture is a blend of the old and the new, from the 2000 year old Cardiff Castle, one of Wales's leading tourist attractions with its enchanting fairytale towers and splendid interior, to the impressive and ultra-modern Wales Millennium Centre, home of Welsh National Opera.

Swansea

Tallizmand
Guest House

Cymru
Wales
★★★★

SB

Wi-Fi

Llanmadoc, Gower, Swansea SA3 1DE
Tel: 01792 386373

Tastefully furnished en suite rooms. Near to beautiful secluded beaches, lined by pine forests and salt marshes. Coastal and inland walks, flowers, birds. Open all year.

B&B from £34.00 sharing a double room

- 3 double rooms (all en suite and recently refurbished to a high standard)
- ground floor rooms available
- no smoking
- special diets catered for
- tea, coffee and TV facilities in each room
- ample parking
- available 12 months a year
- large comfortable guest lounge with real fire

e-mail: tallizmandbb@aol.com
www.tallizmand.co.uk

Aberdeen, Banff & Moray

symbols

Pets Welcome		Children Welcome	
SB Short Breaks		Suitable for Disabled Guests	
Licensed		Wi-Fi Wi-Fi available	

Banchory, Dufftown

Dominated by the Grampian Highlands to the west, extending through Royal Deeside, and with a long coastline along the Moray Firth and the North Sea, Aberdeenshire, Banff and Moray presents a wonderful combination of countryside, coast and heritage for the holidaymaker to explore. Easily accessible from Aberdeen, with all the attractions of city life, this is an ideal corner of the country for an interesting and relaxing break. Why not follow a tourist trail to see the spectacular scenery and learn more about the area at the same time? A visit to this part of Scotland isn't complete without sampling whisky, the national drink, and what better way than to follow the Malt Whisky Trail, visiting distilleries and a traditional cooperage all the way from Forres through the country towns, woodlands and glens of Speyside to remote Glenlivet on the way to the Grampians. Walkers can take a similar route on the Speyside Way from Spey Bay near Buckie up into the mountains. On the Victorian Heritage Trail follow in the footsteps of Queen Victoria to Royal Deeside to reach the best-known castle of all, Balmoral, visiting many of her favourite towns and viewpoints on the way, taking in Crathie Church, still attended by the Royal Family. Golfers have 45 inland courses to choose from, as well as the links courses along the coast. The countryside is ideal for mountain-biking, and there's a network of trails on the on the hills and in the forests of the Glenlivet estate, and all kinds of snow sports are available at Glenshee and the Lecht. Aberdeen, a university city of sparkling granite buildings, has museums, art galleries, theatres, concerts and films, shopping from designer-wear to Scottish crafts, as well as beaches, golf and fishing.

Brechin

Angus & Dundee

Blibberhill Farmhouse

SB

Wi-Fi

Relax and unwind in our traditionally furnished home and lovely garden. Walk along a farm track and experience the wonderful countryside. Peacefully situated between the Cairngorms National Park, glens and coast. Central for golf, fishing riding and walking. Dunottar, Glamis and Edzell Castles nearby. Under 1 hour's drive from Aberdeen, St Andrews and Perth. Cosy in winter. Excellent children's facilities.

Full Scottish breakfast served. Homemade preserves. Traditional Scottish porridge always a favourite. Completely non-smoking house.

All rooms are tastefully decorated and furnished. Clock radios, tea/coffee making facilities, colour TV, electric blankets.

B&B from £27 per person

•Spacious family room, with king-size bed and two single beds. Bath, shower, wc and washbasin en suite.

•Double room, with shower, wc and washbasin en suite.

•Twin/double room with zip-link beds, shower, wc and washbasin en suite.

**Wendy Stewart
Blibberhill Farm
By Brechin DD9 6TH
Tel/Fax: 01307 830323
wendysstewart@aol.com
www.blibberhill.co.uk**

The former Pictish stronghold of Angus stretches from the sand and pebble beaches and rugged cliffs of the North Sea coast inland into the deep, narrow glens at the foothills of the Cairngorm National Park, perfect countryside for walking or for climbing, with ten 'Munros' mountains over 3000 feet, to choose from. The area is a golfers' dream, with a wide choice of courses, from classic links like Carnoustie to the heathland at Edzell in the north and parkland courses nearer the lively coastal city of Dundee. Visit the ancient port of Arbroath during the Sea Fest, celebrating its maritime heritage, and taste a traditional 'smokie'. The more recent past is commemorated in Dundee at Discovery Point, now the home of the RRS Discovery, the ship that took Captain Scott on his ill-fated journey to the Antarctic.

Argyll & Bute

SB

Wi-Fi

01681 700240
Bunessan, Isle of Mull

ARGYLL ARMS

e-mail: argyllarms@isleofmull.co.uk • www.isleofmull.co.uk

The Argyll Arms Hotel, located on the waterfront of the village of Bunessan, and close to the famous Isle of Iona, provides accommodation, bar and restaurant facilities on the beautiful Isle of Mull.

With spectacular sea and island views, the hotel is the perfect base from which to explore, either by car or on foot if walking is your forte, or by bike. We can arrange bike hire or why not bring your own? Secure storage is available and bikers are most welcome. The new owners invite you to enjoy their friendly and relaxed Scottish hospitality in comfortable accommodation, value-for-money bistro-style food and the unique atmosphere of the Isle of Mull. All rooms en suite.

Open all day 365 days of the year catering for residents and non residents.

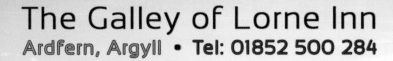

Craignure (Isle of Mull), Dunoon

Argyll & Bute is a wonderfully unspoilt area, historically the birthplace of Scotland and home to a wealth of fascinating wildlife. Here you may be lucky enough to catch a glimpse of an eagle, a wildcat or an osprey, whales, dolphin, seals, or even a giant octopus. At every step the sea fringed landscape is steeped in history, from prehistoric sculpture at Kilmartin and Knapdale, standing stone circles and Bronze Age cup-and-ring engravings, to the elegant ducal home of the once feared Clan Campbell. On the upper reaches of Loch Caolisport can be found St Columba's Cave, and more recent times are illustrated at the Auchindrain Highland Township south of Inveraray, a friendly little town with plenty to see, including the Jail, Wildlife Park and Maritime Museum.

Small, family-run guest house where we aim to make your stay as comfortable as possible. All rooms have central heating, colour TV and hospitality trays; some en suite. A full Scottish breakfast is served, although Continental is available if preferred. We have ample private parking at the rear of the house. Situated 10 minutes' walk from the town centre, train, boat and bus terminals. Oban boasts regular sailings to the Islands, and an excellent golf course, as well as walking, cycling, fishing, or just letting the world go by.

A warm welcome awaits you all year round.

MRS STEWART, GLENVIEW, SOROBA ROAD, OBAN PA34 4JF • Tel: 01631 562267
e-mail: morven.stewart@hotmail.co.uk

A warm welcome awaits you in this delightful bungalow set in 20 acres of farmland where we breed our own Highland cattle which graze at the front. It is a peaceful location as we are set back from the road, and an ideal spot for touring, with the main ferry terminal at Oban just 10 minutes away.

Our luxurious rooms have their own special sitting room attached where you can enjoy your coffee or a glass of wine in peace, and we also have our own restaurant where you can dine.

Mrs J. Currie, Hawthorn, 5 Keil Crofts, Benderloch, Oban PA37 1QS
01631 720452
e-mail: june@hawthorncottages.com
www.hawthorncottages.com

THE
PALACE HOTEL
OBAN

A small, family hotel offering personal supervision, located on Oban's sea front, with wonderful views over the bay, and less than five minutes' walk from the ferry terminal, train and bus station.

The best view in the bay...

Oban, the "Gateway to the Isles", is the ideal base for a West Highland holiday. By boat you can visit the islands of Kerrera, Coll, Tiree, Lismore, Mull and Iona, and by road Glencoe, Ben Nevis and Inveraray.

Fishing, golf, horse riding, sailing, tennis and bowls all nearby.

Built nearly 100 years ago, the hotel has been tastefully modernised and redecorated, while keeping as many of the original features as possible.

13 en suite individually decorated bedrooms, most with FreeSat and large screen TVs and tea/coffee making facilities. WiFi in public areas and bedrooms.

Breakfast is served in the dining room overlooking the bay. Packed lunches available when requested in advance.

Well behaved pets welcome. Reductions for children.

The Palace Hotel
George Street, Oban, Argyll PA34 5SB
Tel: 01631 562294 • Fax: 01631 562863

www.palacehoteloban.co.uk

Rothesay

Ayrshire
& Arran

Beith

Ayr

Brodick

West Tannacrieff

Fenwick, Kilmarnock KA3 6AZ
Tel: 01560 600258
mobile: 07773 226332
Fax: 01560 600914

Wi-Fi

Mrs Nancy Cuthbertson

A warm welcome awaits all our guests to our dairy farm, situated in the peaceful Ayrshire countryside. Relax in spacious, well-furnished, en suite rooms with all modern amenities, colour TV and tea/coffee making facilities. Large parking area and garden.

Situated off the M/A77 on the B751 road to Kilmaurs, so easily accessible from Glasgow, Prestwick Airport, and the south. An ideal base for exploring Ayrshire's many tourist attractions.

Enjoy a hearty breakfast with home-made breads and preserves, and home baking for supper. Children welcome. Terms from £30 per person. Brochure available.

e-mail: westtannacrieff@btopenworld.com
www.smoothhound.co.uk/hotels/westtannacrieff.html

Open all year
Terms from £24pppn

SUNNYSIDE – a very special place to stay with its south easterly unrestricted rural and coastal views across the bonny Clyde on the beautiful Isle of Arran. Enjoy this view over a scrumptious full breakfast; relax in the comfort and cleanliness of the double en suite, or twin bedded room (with private bathroom) both having shower over bath. Located in Kings Cross, 8 miles south of Brodick; and convenient for good restaurants/pubs.

SB

Mrs Evelyn Coles, "Sunnyside"
King's Cross, Isle of Arran KA27 8RG
Tel: 01770 700422 or 0771 800 5688
e-mail: evelyncoles@mypostoffice.co.uk
www.britishholidaysdirect.co.uk

Ayrshire and The Isle of Arran in Scotland's south west is flanked by Dumfries and Galloway to the south and the Central Belt to the north. As well as long-established seaside resorts like Ayr and Largs, the area is best known for sailing and golf, including three Open Championship courses, and of course, Robert Burns, Scotland's national poet, whose life and works are celebrated at the Burns National Heritage Park at Alloway. The Isle of Arran, as well as being one of Scotland's most accessible islands, is also arguably one of its most truly representative. From the mountainous north to the undulating south it is easy to see how the island became known as "Scotland in miniature", making it a favourite holiday destination for walking, wildlife and simply relaxing.

SB

South Whittlieburn Farmhouse B&B
and Caravan & Camping,
Brisbane Glen, Largs KA30 8SN
Tel: 01475 675881 • Fax: 01475 675080

Superb farmhouse accommodation with lovely scenic views on our working sheep farm in peaceful Brisbane Glen. Ample parking. Only five minutes' drive from the popular tourist resort of Largs and near the ferries to the islands. 40 minutes from Glasgow and Prestwick airports. Warm friendly hospitality, enormous delicious breakfasts. All rooms en suite.

Chosen by "WHICH? TOP TEN BEST BED & BREAKFAST", WELCOME HOST.

Nominated for AA LANDLADY OF THE YEAR 2005 & 06 • BEST BREAKFAST AWARD 2003 & 2011

Bed & Breakfast from £31pppn.

Caravan and camping site on our farm 2½ miles north east of Largs; electric hook-ups, toilet and shower, from £13 per night. Caravan for hire. Also self-catering flat available at Dunoon. Open all year except Christmas.

A warm welcome from Mary Watson. Enjoy a great holiday at South Whittlieburn Farm, for a holiday you will want to repeat where guests become friends.

e-mail: largsbandb@southwhittlieburnfarm.freeserve.co.uk

www.ukcampsite.co.uk

www.SmoothHound.co.uk/hotels/whittlie.html

SB

A warm welcome awaits you at our family farm situated in the beautiful Doon Valley. An ideal base for touring Ayrshire or Galloway on the Galloway Tourist Route (A713), 6 miles south of Ayr.

Our spacious farmhouse offers en suite twin/double and family rooms with king size beds and all facilities, lounge, dining room and large garden. We serve a delicious varied farmhouse breakfast, with homebaking and farm produce in season. Enjoy a bedtime tea/coffee or hot chocolate with a home baked cookie. Prestwick Airport guests welcome (whatever the time!). Children and pets welcome. B&B from £22.50 pppn, children half price.

Smithston Farm, Patna, By Ayr KA6 7EZ
Mrs Joyce Bothwell - 01292 531211
e-mail: bothwellfarming@mail.com
www.smithstonfarmhouse.co.uk

Prestwick

North Beach
Hotel

5-7 Links Road, Prestwick KA9 1QG
Tel: 01292 479069
Fax: 01292 671521
info@northbeach.co.uk
www.northbeach.co.uk

- Free Park - Stay - Fly
- Central location: a few minutes away from Prestwick Airport
- Overlooking the famous Prestwick Golf Course
- Majority of our rooms have spectacular views of the golf course
- The perfect base from which to tour first-class Ayrshire courses
- Our restaurant serves a multi-cuisine menu and a variety of over 50 malts in our licensed bar

Open all year • Single from £39.50 B&B, Double/Twin from £69.50 B&B

Borders

Jedburgh

Hundalee House
Jedburgh TD8 6PA Tel & Fax: 01835 863011

Large historic Manor House set in 15 acres of secluded gardens and woodland near Jedburgh, decorated in a charming Victorian style. All rooms are en suite, one with four-poster, and all with the expected luxuries including TV, tea/coffee making facilities, hairdryer, central heating, free wireless internet. Children welcome.

Wi-Fi

Bed and Breakfast from £28-£30 per person per night. Single £30-£45. Reductions for children.
e-mail: sheila.whittaker@btinternet.com • www.accommodation-scotland.org

SB

Wi-Fi

SB

Melrose

SB

Wi-Fi

Crossed by the River Tweed, which provides some of the best fishing in Scotland, the Scottish Borders stretch from the rolling hills and moorland in the west, through gentler valleys and agricultural plains, to the rocky Berwickshire coastline with its secluded coves and picturesque fishing villages. This variety of landscape has led to numerous opportunities for walking, horse riding and cycling, fishing and golf, as well as surfing, diving and birdwatching on the coast. Friendly towns, long known for their textiles, and charming villages are there to be discovered, while castles, abbeys, stately homes and museums illustrate the exciting and often bloody history of the area, commemorated in the Common Ridings and other local festivals which create a colourful pageant much enjoyed by visitors and native Borderers alike.

Peebles

SB

Wi-Fi

Warm, modern farmhouse B&B set in delightful walled garden in the heart of the Scottish Borders. Three spacious suites; also one double/twin and one single bedroom, all with private bathroom. Good home cooking using local produce. Loch fishing; grazing for horses; ideal for walking, cycling and horse riding. Clay target shooting nearby. Well behaved pets welcome. Edinburgh one hour's drive. Open all year.

The Garden House, Whitmuir, Selkirk TD7 4PZ
Tel: 01750 721728 • Mobile: 07768 707700
e-mail: whitmuir@btconnect.com
www.whitmuirfarm.co.uk

The Meadows is a modern four-bedroom detached house located in a quiet situation near the centre of the conservation village of West Linton, which is on the A702, the main Edinburgh to Carlisle road, with handy access to Edinburgh and central Scotland.

All bedrooms have tea/coffee making facilities, TV and hairdryer.

Full range of quality breakfasts available including traditional English or scrambled egg with smoked salmon and oatcakes. Evening meals available by prior arrangement. Pets welcome. Parking.

Terms from £25pppn twin, £30pppn single, £30pppn double/twin en suite.

Mrs M. Thain, The Meadows Bed and Breakfast, 4 Robinsland Drive, West Linton EH46 7JD
01968 661798 • e-mail: mwthain@btinternet.com
www.themeadowsbandb.co.uk

West Linton

SB

Wi-Fi

Drochil Castle B&B

Family-run Drochil Castle is a traditional Scottish farmhouse offering a relaxed, friendly welcome. In summer sit and enjoy the view over the garden with its handsome mature trees.
If the weather is less kind unwind by the fireside and enjoy a cup of tea and some home-baking.
Drochil is ideally placed for touring the scenic and historic Scottish border country with its delightful towns, especially Peebles, Melrose and Kelso.
The house is traditionally decorated, very comfortable, warm and welcoming. Every attempt has been made to anticipate your needs. All the bedrooms have tea and coffee making facilities, TV, radio alarm and electric blankets. All linen and towels are provided. Public rooms have comfy sofas and in cooler weather a roaring fire entices guests into the sitting room. Breakfast is served in the conservatory with its spectacular panoramic view.

Ann Black • Drochil Castle B&B
Drochil Castle Farm, Romanno Bridge
Peebles EH46 7DD
Tel: 01721 752249
e-mail: annblack@drochilcastle.co.uk
www.drochilcastle.co.uk

Dumfries & Galloway

Castle Douglas

SB

DEESIDE Bed & Breakfast

Small, family-run accommodation, surrounded by the unspoiled beauty of the Galloway countryside. One double en suite, twin/double with private facilities.
The surrounding area has something for everyone, from walking along the coast with its stunning scenery to mountain biking.

42 Main Street, Castle Douglas DG7 3AU • Tel: 01556 670239
info@deesidebandb.co.uk • deesidexm@aol.com • www.deesidebandb.co.uk

symbols 🐕🐎 SB ♿ ♉ Wi-Fi

🐕	*Pets Welcome*	🐎	*Children Welcome*
SB	*Short Breaks*	♿	*Suitable for Disabled Guests*
♉	*Licensed*	**Wi-Fi**	*Wi-Fi available*

Wigtown

SB

Wi-Fi

HILLCREST HOUSE

Maidland Place, Wigtown DG8 9EU
Tel: 01988 402018

Full of character and charm, this stunning Victorian villa has been carefully restored with your comfort in mind, with six comfortable en suite bedrooms and an elegant guest lounge. Award-winning evening meals using fresh local produce are available in the spacious dining room.

There are fabulous views over the largest nature reserve in Britain, Wigtown Bay Nature Reserve; nearby, the Galloway Forest Park offers a wealth of wildlife and miles of adventure paradise, including mountain biking centres and waymarked trails. At night, it is one of the best spots for stargazing as it is the first Dark Sky Park in the UK and one of only two in Europe.

e-mail: info@hillcrest-wigtown.co.uk
www.hillcrest-wigtown.co.uk

Dumfries & Galloway combines high moorland and sheltered glens, forests, sandy beaches, crags, cliffs and rocky shores, presenting abundant opportunities for hill walking, rambling, fishing for salmon and sea trout, cycling, mountain biking, off-road driving, horse riding, pony trekking and bird watching. Catch a glimpse of a red kite soaring above, or a wild goat or red squirrel in the 300 square miles of the Galloway Forest Park or hunt for sea life in a rocky coastal pool. Golfers can choose from 30 courses, whether the challenging links at Southerness or a local course with spectacular views. Warmed by the influence of the Gulf Stream, touring in this quiet corner of south west Scotland is a pleasure, visiting the dozens of interesting castles, gardens, museums and historic sites. In addition a never-ending succession of music festivals, ceilidhs, village fairs, country dances, classical music concerts and children's entertainment guarantees plenty of scope for enjoyment, and for those whose interest is in the night skies a visit to the Galloway Forest Park, the UK's first designated Dark Sky Park, is a 'must'. Discover the many hidden secrets of this lovely and unspoilt landscape such as the pretty little villages along the coast, including the 'Artists' Town', Kirkcudbright, while those who love 'the written word' must surely visit the book town of Wigtown.

Bathgate, Edinburgh

Edinburgh & Lothians

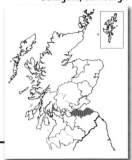

This 17th century farmhouse is situated two miles from M8 Junction 4, which is midway between Glasgow and Edinburgh. This peaceful location overlooks panoramic views of the countryside. All rooms are on the ground floor, ideal for disabled visitors, and have central heating, colour TV and tea/coffee making facilities. We are within easy reach of golf, fishing, cycling (15 mile cycle track runs along back of property).

SB

Scottish TOURIST BOARD ★★★ B&B

Ample security parking.
Open January to December.
Children and pets by arrangement
Twin Room from £44-£55,
Family Room £60-£80

Mrs F. Gibb, Tarrareoch Farm, Station Road, Armadale, Near Bathgate EH48 3BJ Tel: 01501 730404 nicola@gibb0209.fsnet.co.uk

---

INTERNATIONAL GUEST HOUSE • EDINBURGH

Conveniently situated 1½ miles south of Princes Street on the main A701, on the main bus route. Private parking. All bedrooms en suite, with direct-dial telephone, colour TV and tea/coffee making facilities. Some rooms enjoy magnificent views across to the extinct volcano of Arthur's Seat. The full Scottish breakfasts served on the finest bone china are a delight.

SB

B&B from £45 to £85 single; £70 to £150 double.

37 Mayfield Gardens, Edinburgh EH9 2BX Tel: 0131 667 2511 • Fax: 0131 667 1112

AA ★★★★ Guest House

e-mail: intergh1@yahoo.co.uk • www.accommodation-edinburgh.com

SB

Wi-Fi

Ravensdown Guest House

Ravensdown is a friendly and stylish guest house, run by David (Scottish) and Yoka (Dutch), which provides excellent value, high quality bed and breakfast accommodation in central Edinburgh. A spacious Edwardian house built in the early 1900s, Ravensdown has spectacular views of the city skyline, Edinburgh Castle and Arthur's Seat.

There are seven well-appointed, spacious guest bedrooms - double, twin, triple and family - all of which are en suite. The front bedrooms have fantastic views of Edinburgh.

Wireless internet access throughout • Choice of Continental, Scottish or vegetarian breakfast Dutch and English spoken • Ample free car parking

Contact: David and Yoka, Ravensdown Guest House, 248 Ferry Road, Edinburgh EH5 3AN
Tel: 0131 552 5438 • e-mail: david@ravensdownhouse.com
www.ravensdownhouse.com

Wi-Fi

Only 3 miles from Edinburgh Airport and 4 miles from the city centre, this detached bungalow is in an ideal location. There is a good bus service into the centre of Edinburgh and we have free off-street parking available. We are a non-smoking establishment. We can provide single, twin, double and multiple accommodation.
All rooms have a private entrance; en suite facilities; television; hospitality tray; fridge; hairdryer; iron; etc. Breakfast is served in your room (cooked or Continental). Rates from £30 per person.

Ingleneuk

31 Drum Brae North, Edinburgh EH4 8AT
Tel: 0131 317 1743
e-mail: ingleneukbnb@btinternet.com
www.ingleneukbandb.co.uk

Pathhead, Portobello

Anstruther

Fife

The Kingdom of Fife - and more particularly the coastal university town of St Andrews – is
renowned worldwide as the home of golf, where not only the famous links, but parkland and
heathland courses number among more than 40 available for golfers to choose from. The
south of this small, self-contained former county has been dominated by the Forth Road and
Rail Bridges, the imposing road and rail links with Edinburgh and the south, but the sandy
beaches and traditional fishing villages at places like Elie, Crail, Pittenweem, and Aberdour
are major attractions for holidaymakers. At North Queensferry families will love the
excitement of Deep Sea World with its Underwater Safari and seal sanctuary. The historic
associations of centres like Dunfermline, Scotland's former capital, the restored medieval
village of Culross and the Palace of Falkland are just some of many fascinating places to visit.

Leven

Glasgow & District

In one of Europe's most dynamic cultural centres, there's so much to see and do – from the City of Glasgow itself, alive with heritage, architecture, entertainment and nightlife, to the charm of the bustling towns, scenic villages and countryside of the surrounding districts. James Watt, Adam Smith, Charles Rennie Mackintosh, Lord Kelvin and a host of others have all played a major part in Greater Glasgow's past. Today the area has a wealth of attractions which recall their works. Entertainment and sport feature in an exciting year round calendar that encompasses opera and theatre, music of all kinds, Scottish ceilidhs and top sporting events. One of the UK's top shopping centres, Glasgow is home to a multitude of shops, from boutiques and specialist stores, to the High Street favourites, and shopping malls. Out in the easily accessible countryside, follow the famous River Clyde from New Lanark, the site of the historic 18th century mills established by Robert Owen.

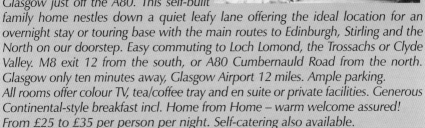

Highlands

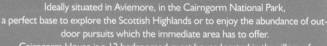

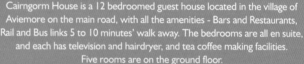

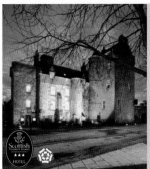

Fort William

Wi-Fi

Innishfree
Lochyside,
Fort William PH33 7NX

Set against the background of Ben Nevis, this spacious Bed and Breakfast house offers a high level of service. Just two miles from the town centre and three miles from Glen Nevis. Visitors are guaranteed a warm friendly welcome and excellent accommodation. All rooms have en suite facilities and also offer remote-control colour TV and tea/coffee making facilities. Breakfast is served in the conservatory, which is overlooked by panoramic views. Enthusiastic advice on pursuits and activities are given. Access to private car park is available. This house has a non-smoking policy and pets are not allowed. Open all year. *Prices from £30 per person per night.*

Scottish
TOURIST BOARD
★★★★
B&B

Mrs Mary MacLean • Tel: 01397 70547
e-mail: mburnsmaclean@aol.com
www.innishfree.co.uk

SB

Scottish
TOURIST BOARD
★★★★
GUEST HOUSE

Braeburn B&B

Stunning views over Loch Linnhe and the Ardgour Hills.

A warm welcome awaits you in this spacious, family-run house with panoramic views of the surrounding area. Ben Nevis is only four miles away and can be clearly seen from the house. Situated in its own private grounds with ample off-road parking and storage for bikes and skiing equipment. Relax in our comfortable residents' lounge or on our sunny patio. Enjoy a hearty breakfast to set you up for the day.

We are 3 miles from the town centre and we have a hotel and bars nearby, all serving good food and drink. Ideally situated for touring the West Highlands of Scotland.

En suite rooms ❖ TV ❖ Hospitality tray ❖ Hairdryer
Prices range from £30 per person ❖ Open all year
Badabrie, Fort William PH33 7LX • 01397 772047
e-mail: enquiries@braeburnfortwilliam.co.uk
www.braeburnfortwilliam.co.uk

Welcome to Ossian's • Fort William

Ossian's Hotel is the place to stay in Fort William, a friendly and informal base for your holiday, with shops, restaurants, pubs, museum, library, internet café, bus and railway station, swimming pool, leisure centre, the Old Fort, Loch Linnhe…all within a 5 minute walk.

Whether you are walking the West Highland Way, or the Great Glen Way, climbing Ben Nevis, or just enjoying some of the most spectacular scenery without being energetic, then this is the perfect place to stay.

Double, twin, single, and family rooms are available, all en suite, with TV and tea tray. The restaurant serves traditional Scottish home cooking and the lounge bar is open all day and evening, for drinks, coffees and snacks.

•We are a family-run guest house situated in the Highland village of Ballachulish. Set on the shores of Loch Leven and only one mile from the majesty of Glencoe, Ballachulish makes an

ideal centre for exploring much of Scotland's natural beauty. Attractions in and around Glencoe, Fort William, Oban, Skye, Mull, Loch Ness, Loch Lomond and many others are easily accessible.

Imposing craggy mountains, beautiful lochs, waterfalls and forestry can all be found locally and wildlife such as seals, dolphins, otters, deer, pine-martens and eagles thrive.There are a multitude of beautiful and interesting walks, from strolls to view historic Glencoe or around the Lochan trails to mainland Britain's most challenging mountain ridge - Glencoe's Aonach Eagach (The Notched Ridge).

•All of our rooms have en suite facilities, colour TV, DVD player, hospitality tray and individually controlled room heaters.

•We have a comfortable guest lounge, snack bar, separate dining room, drying room, bike store and large car park.

•Free Wi-Fi internet access available.

•Easy to find, next door to the Tourist Information Centre.

•B&B from £20.

Mike and Christine Richardson
Strathassynt Guest House, Loanfern,
Ballachulish, Near Glencoe PH49 4JB
Tel: 01855 811261
e-mail: info@strathassynt.com
www.strathassynt.com

SB

Wi-Fi

ARDSELMA
Bed & Breakfast • Kingussie

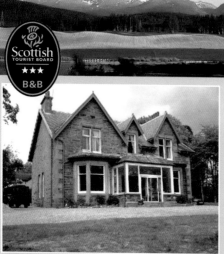

Ardselma is a late 19th century Victorian hunting lodge, tastefully decorated and furnished, now a family run guesthouse offering bed and breakfast. Dinner and packed lunches can be provided by prior arrangement.

It is situated within 3 acres of private grounds, ensuring peace and tranquillity, with ample parking and safe bicycle storage.

There are five very spacious and comfortable bedrooms, most of which are double or king size, with en suite or private bathroom. Tea and coffee making facilities are available in the dining room, after which why not retire to the sitting room where an open log fire awaits.

Only 3 minutes' walk from the centre of the Highland village of Kingussie, convenient for those travelling by car, rail or coach. Nearby there are numerous visitor attractions and activities such as golf, horse riding, hill walking, bird watching and much more.

- Groups catered for, discounts available
- Children and pets welcome
- Bed and Breakfast from £28pppn.

Valerie J. Johnston,
Ardselma, The Crescent, Kingussie PH21 1JZ
Tel: 077866 96384 • Mobile: 07786 696384
e-mail: valerieardselma@aol.com
www.kingussiebedandbreakfast.co.uk

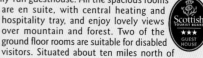

Hill View

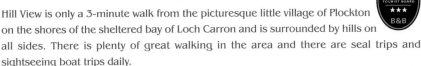

Situated in a quiet area with views across the Applecross Hills, Hill View offers cosy, en suite accommodation with a real Highland welcome. You can sit in the garden and enjoy the views (snacks and BBQ available). For breakfast, the choice is yours - Continental, full Scottish breakfast, kippers etc.

Scottish
TOURIST BOARD
★★★
B&B

Hill View is only a 3-minute walk from the picturesque little village of Plockton on the shores of the sheltered bay of Loch Carron and is surrounded by hills on all sides. There is plenty of great walking in the area and there are seal trips and sightseeing boat trips daily.

The railway station is only a mile away from Hill View (lifts available) and there are plenty of eating places nearby.

From £27.50 per person per night • £55 for double room with two people sharing.

Mrs Sybil Cameron, Hill View, 2 Frithard Road, Plockton IV52 8TQ • Tel & Fax: 01599 544226
e-mail: cameron_sybil@yahoo.co.uk

Poolewe • Wester Ross

Bruach Ard overlooks beautiful Loch Ewe at Inverasdale near Poolewe in Wester Ross. We are an informal, family-run B&B (non-smoking), comprising two double bedrooms and one twin bedroom (all en suite), comfortable guest sitting room with TV (Sky connected), video, board games, CD player, local guidebooks, maps and brochures. The sitting room and guest dining room overlook the Loch. Full cooked and/or continental breakfast. Fresh local produce is used where possible. Packed lunches by arrangement. Pets welcome. STB ★★★ B&B.

e-mail: dgeorge@globalnet.co.uk
Tel: 01445 781765 • www.davidgeorge.co.uk

SB

The Old Inn at Reay in Caithness is truly a piece of Scottish history. It was originally built in 1739 as an Inn serving both travellers and the people of the village of Reay. The original building is still intact and in use as a private home and a bed and breakfast establishment today. Jean and Derek Murray are your hosts at The Old Inn and their objective is to make your stay a very special one. To this end, they have developed bedrooms to keep you comfortable, and both a breakfast and evening menu to make you feel very special indeed. Ideal base for touring the far north of Scotland, or catching the ferry to Orkney.

Scottish
TOURIST BOARD
★★★
B&B

The Old Inn

Reay, Thurso KW14 7RE

derek.theoldinn@btinternet.com
www.theoldinnatreay.co.uk
Tel: 01847 811554

SB

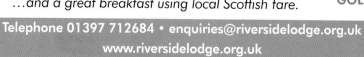

This former 19th century coaching inn on the John O'Groats peninsula is set in six acres of parkland, close to the Queen Mother's former Highland home, the Castle of Mey.

Fully modernised, the hotel has eight centrally heated en suite bedrooms with colour television and tea making facilities; the spacious Pentland Suite offers a double and family room with en suite bathroom.

Locally caught salmon, crab and other fine Highland produce feature on the varied table d'hôte and grill menus available in the Garden Room, while lighter meals and snacks can be enjoyed in the cosy Pentland Lounge.

A warm Highland welcome awaits you.

www.castlearms.co.uk
Tel & Fax: 01847 851244
e-mail: castlearms.mey@btinternet.com

Scottish TOURIST BOARD ★★ SMALL HOTEL

THE CASTLE ARMS
HOTEL
Mey, By Thurso,
Caithness KW14 8XH

Apart from the stunning and varied scenery, the major attraction of The Scottish Highlands is that there is so much to see and do, whatever the season. Stretching from Fort William in the south, to Wick in the far north, and with access links radiating out from the busy city of Inverness, there is a wealth of visitor attractions and facilities. Perhaps the most famous is Loch Ness, home of the legendary monster, and a good starting point for a sail down the Caledonian Canal, through the unspoiled scenery of the Great Glen to Fort William. Just to the south lies Ben Nevis, Glencoe and a whole range of outdoor sporting activities from fishing and sailing to skiing. In the Cairngorm National Park it's possible to glimpse an osprey or capercaillie while walking, climbing, skiing or cycling, or just enjoying the stunning mountain scenery.

THE FERRY BOAT INN &

THE
FRIGATE

We welcome you to The Ferry Boat Inn on the shorefront in Ullapool. All of our 9 bedrooms are en suite and we offer Bar Meals or fine dining in our beautiful Restaurant.

**Ferry Boat Inn
Shore Street
Ullapool IV26 2UJ
Tel: 01854 612 366
www.ferryboat-inn.com**

THE FRIGATE CAFÉ & BISTRO

High quality licensed Bistro, Café,Outside Caterers, Deli, Bakery and Take Away

Frigate Café, Shore Street, Ullapool, IV26 2UJ
Tel: 01854 612 969
www.ullapoolcatering.co.uk

Lanark

Lanarkshire

St Catherines
Bed & Breakfast

Contact: Mrs B. McMillan
1 Kenilworth Road,
Lanark ML11 7BL
Tel/Fax: 01555 662295
Mobile: 07963 779501

Scottish
TOURIST BOARD
★★★
B&B

Wi-Fi

At St Catherines you will be assured of a warm welcome and hearty breakfast, whether it be cooked, Continental or vegetarian. The rooms are tastefully decorated and are en suite; all with TV, radio, hairdryer, and complimentary tea tray with snacks etc. We are in a central position a few minutes walk from both bus and train stations, and shops and restaurants.

Lanark has historic links with William Wallace and is a good touring base for Glasgow, Edinburgh and the surrounding area which has many golf courses. Near the New Lanark World Heritage Village. Prices are from £25pp. Please note there is no smoking anywhere in the house.

e-mail: stcatherinesbb@yahoo.co.uk   www.st-catherines.co.uk

Lesmahagow

A modern farmhouse bungalow on Dykecroft Farm, set in lovely surroundings in a rural area on the B7086 (old A726) and within easy reach of the M74, making it the ideal stop between north and south; also convenient for Glasgow and Prestwick airports. Centrally situated for touring Glasgow, Edinburgh, Ayr, Stirling and New Lanark - all within one hour's drive. Nearby is Strathclyde Country Park with all watersports activities; other sporting facilities within two miles include sports centre, golf, fishing, quad bikes, rifle and clay pigeon shooting, and swimming. Guests will enjoy the open fires in our TV lounge and the good breakfasts; TV and tea making facilities in all rooms. A warm and friendly welcome awaits all guests.

Dykecroft Farm

**Boghead, Kirkmuirhill,
Lesmahagow ML11 0JQ**
e-mail: Dykecroft.bandb@tiscali.co.uk

Tel & Fax: 01555 892226
www.Dykecroftfarm.co.uk

Perth & Kinross

Blairgowrie

Holmrigg B&B

One double, one double four-poster and one double/twin on ground floor. All rooms en suite with tea/coffee making facilities, radio and TV; ironing and hair drying facilities. Comfortable lounge with colour TV; diningroom. Heating throughout. Vegetarian meals; home cooking and baking; full cooked breakfast. Places of interest range from Scott's 'Discovery' in Dundee to Edinburgh Castle. Also golf, fishing and walking. Pets by arrangement.

B&B from £28.50 to £30pp, discounts for Senior Citizens.
**Rosalind Young, Holmrigg, Wester
Essendy, Blairgowrie PH10 6RD
Tel & Fax: 01250 884309
e-mail: info@holmrigg.co.uk
www.holmrigg-bnb.co.uk**

CLACHAN COTTAGE HOTEL

Lochearnhead, Perthshire FK19 8PU

- Friendly, family-run hotel in spectacular lochside setting.
- Well placed in Central Scotland for touring.
- Many golf courses within an hour's drive.
- 30 Munros within 30 minutes.
- Water-sports available from the hotel.

AWARD-WINNING TASTE OF SCOTLAND
RESTAURANT • GROUP/SOCIETY RATES

•PETS WELCOME•

Tel: 01567 830247

Fax: 01567 830300

info@clachancottagehotel.co.uk

www.clachancottagehotel.co.uk

SB

Wi-Fi

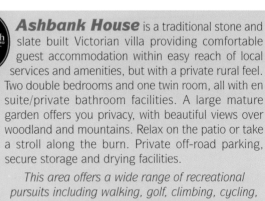

Scottish
TOURIST BOARD
★★★
B&B

Ashbank House is a traditional stone and slate built Victorian villa providing comfortable guest accommodation within easy reach of local services and amenities, but with a private rural feel. Two double bedrooms and one twin room, all with en suite/private bathroom facilities. A large mature garden offers you privacy, with beautiful views over woodland and mountains. Relax on the patio or take a stroll along the burn. Private off-road parking, secure storage and drying facilities.

This area offers a wide range of recreational pursuits including walking, golf, climbing, cycling, motor biking, water sports, fishing, whisky tasting and many more. Other attractions: dam with fish ladder, Pitlochry Festival Theatre.

B&B from £25pppn.

Ashbank House, 14 Tomcroy Terrace,
Pitlochry PH16 5JA
Tel: 01796 472711
e-mail: ashbankhouse@btinternet.com
www.ashbankhouse.co.uk

Stanley

Newmill Farm

Stanley PH1 4PS

Mrs Ann Guthrie • 01738 828281

e-mail: guthrienewmill@sol.co.uk

www.newmillfarm.co.uk

This 330 acre farm is situated on the A9, six miles north of Perth. Accommodation comprises twin and double en suite rooms and a family room with private bathroom; lounge, sittingroom, diningroom; bathroom, shower room and toilet. Bed and Breakfast from £30 .
The warm welcome and supper of excellent home baking are inclusive. Reductions and facilities for children. Pets accepted. Ample car parking area. Excellent local restaurants nearby.

The numerous castles and historic ruins around Perth are testimony to Scotland's turbulent past. Situated in the area known as "The Gateway to the Highlands" the farm is ideally placed for those seeking some of the best unspoilt scenery in Western Europe. Many famous golf courses and trout rivers in the Perth area. If walking or cycling are your interests, there are plenty of routes around the farm that are worth exploring to enjoy the views.

SB

Wi-Fi

Tayside Hotel

• Hotel • Bar • Restaurant • Function Room

Mill Street, Stanley,
Perthshire PH1 4NL
www.taysidehotel.co.uk
reception@taysidehotel.co.uk
01738 82 82 49

Warm hospitality and delicious home cooked cuisine: a wonderful short break destination as well as a home from home for an extended Scottish vacation.
Come and stay in one of our 12 en suite guest rooms for a short break or longer escape. While you're with us try your hand at some local activities including salmon fishing, golf, river rafting or Highland safaris... sample a wee dram at one of the many local whisky distilleries... or simply slow down and enjoy some of the beautiful Perthshire landscape.
All rooms Twin or Double en suite
Bed and Breakfast or Half-board basis available • Dogs welcome

Callander

Stirling & The Trossachs

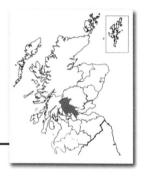

symbols ★ ⮝ SB ♿ ♀ Wi-Fi

🐕	*Pets Welcome*	🐎	*Children Welcome*
SB	*Short Breaks*	♿	*Suitable for Disabled Guests*
♀	*Licensed*	Wi-Fi	*Wi-Fi available*

Strathyre

At the heart of Scotland, Stirling, Loch Lomond and the Trossachs combines history and scenic beauty, and endless opportunities for walking, cycling and boating, all within an hour of Edinburgh and Glasgow. Stirling Castle, magnificently restored to tell the story of this former seat of Scottish monarchs, provides a panoramic view from Ben Lomond across the Trossachs and over Bannockburn and other battlegrounds so important in Scotland's history. A walk through the medieval Old Town of Stirling, Scotland's newest city, is the ideal starting point for touring the area, then explore the wild glens and sparkling lochs in Loch Lomond and The Trossachs National Park, and perhaps take a steamer trip down Loch Katrine. Whatever your fitness, there are walks suitable for everyone, cycle routes, challenging mountain bike trails, golf and wildlife. The amazing Falkirk Wheel linking the Forth and Clyde and Union Canals is a sight and experience not to be missed, while villages and small towns such as Drymen, Killearn, Fintry and Kippen offer hospitality and interesting outings less than an hour from Glasgow, yet feels worlds apart from the bustle of city life.

Scottish Islands

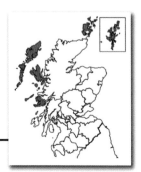

SB

REDBURN HOUSE
Lochmaddy, North Uist

Redburn House is a Bed and Breakfast establishment in Lochmaddy, the main township of the wonderful Hebridean Isle of North Uist. Redburn House offers four en suite Bed and Breakfast rooms, a self-catering cottage (the Boat House), a self-catering annexe (the Studio) and a large self-catering Apartment.

Redburn House has recently undergone extensive renovation which has transformed it into the warm, cosy, clean and modern guesthouse it is now.

It is ideally located close to the post office, pub, Arts Centre, Sailing Club, Outdoor Centre, shop, Tourist Information Centre and Ferry Terminal.

**Contact Maggie at
info@redburnhouse.com
Tel/Fax: 01876 500301 or
Redburn House,
Lochmaddy, Isle of North Uist,
Western Isles HS6 5AA
www.redburnhouse.com**

So many islands are waiting to be visited off the Scottish mainland, each with a mystery and magic of its own. To the north lie the Orkney and Shetland Isles, with their strong connections to the Vikings whose influence is still seen and heard today. To the west, exposed to the Atlantic, lie the Inner and Outer Hebrides, including the islands of Skye, Islay, Mull and Tiree, Lewis, Harris and Barra, each with its own culture, traditions and heritage. Everywhere there's evidence of settlement going back to prehistoric times, including awe-inspiring standing stones and circles and chambered cairns. Some islands have mountains to climb, but most are low-lying, ideal for exploring on foot and for cycling and bird watching, while the Atlantic waves have proved a great attraction to surfers from all over the world.

Broadford

Hillview is a large house with stunning views over Broadford Bay towards Torridon and Applecross.
The B&B has a double bedroom with en suite facilities, a double bedroom with shared facilities, and a twin room with shared facilities, as well as a family room with a private bathroom and a balcony. We offer a full Scottish breakfast or vegetarian option if you prefer. Our rooms are very comfortable and most have stunning sea views.

Hillview B&B is an ideal base for exploring surrounding area. The scenery is wild and dramatic, with the Cuillin range being the island's most famous feature. The landscape varies from the strange rock formations of the Quirang to the lushness of the Garden of Skye in the south of the island. Around Broadford there are numerous mountain and coastal walks for all abilities.

Isabel MacLeod, Hillview, Blackpark, Broadford, Isle of Skye IV49 9DE
e-mail: isabel@hillview-skye.co.uk • Telephone: 01471 822 083
www.hillview-skye.co.uk

Whichever way you approach the Isle of Skye, whether by ferry from Mallaig in the south or over the Skye Bridge, the scene will be dominated by the majestic Red and Black Cuillin, attracting climbers from all over the world. At lower levels, scramble over the foothills, or explore the inlets and bays, keeping watch for the wildlife on land and along the coastal waters. Historic castles bear witness to the turbulent history of the island, dating back even to the brochs of Neolithic times. At Staffin Bay in the north stand in the footprints of dinosaurs, visit the museum and perhaps find fossil evidence yourself. With good ferry connections from Uig to the Harris and Uist, use your visit as a stepping stone to explore the outer Hebridean islands too.

Please note...

All the information in this book is given in good faith in the belief that it is correct. However, the publishers cannot guarantee the facts given in these pages, neither are they responsible for changes in policy, ownership or terms that may take place after the date of going to press. Readers should always satisfy themselves that the facilities they require are available and that the terms, if quoted, still apply.

Pubs & Inns

A selection of inns, pubs and hostelries offering food, refreshment and traditional good cheer; many also provide comfortable overnight accommodation.

🛏 Accommodation available   **Wi-Fi** Wi-Fi available

🍽 Food available   🐕 Pets welcome

🅿 Parking   🎠 Children welcome

Ely

THE ANCHOR INN

Sutton Gault, Near Ely, Cambridgeshire CB6 2BD
Tel: 01353 778537 • Fax: 01353 776180
e-mail: anchorinn@popmail.bta.com
www.anchor-inn-restaurant.co.uk

The 17th Century Anchor Inn offers modern British cuisine with an emphasis on seasonal and traditional ingredients; superb wine list. We have four guest bedrooms offering a variety of accommodation to suit every need.
The Anchor is ideally situated for exploring East Anglia; it is only 7 miles from Ely and is less than half an hour from Cambridge. Newmarket and its racecourse are within easy reach.

Mawgan

The Falcon Inn

The Falcon Inn,
St Mawgan TR8 4EP
Tel: 01637 860225

AA
★★★★
INN

Sarah and David would like to welcome you to The Falcon Inn, St Mawgan. We hope that you will enjoy a visit with us, whether it is just for a meal and a drink, or for a longer stay. The Inn comprises a bar area and separate restaurant. Outside there is a large well-kept garden.
There are also covered areas outside for eating alfresco.
The Falcon Inn has two luxury letting rooms: one double room and one twin room. The rooms are furnished to the highest standard and we pride ourselves on providing value for money. Each room contains tea/coffee making facilities, colour TV and telephone. Guide dogs only.

🛏
🍽
🅿
Wi-Fi
🎠

e-mail: thefalconinnstmawgan@gmail.com
www.thefalconinnstmawgan.co.uk

Eaton

The Plough
AT EATON

**Macclesfield Road, Eaton,
Near Congleton, Cheshire CW12 2NH
Tel: 01260 280207 • Fax: 01260 298458**

AA
★ ★ ★ ★
INN

Traditional oak beams and blazing log fires in winter reflect the warm and friendly atmosphere of this half-timbered former coaching inn which dates from the 17th century.

The heart of the 'Plough' is the kitchen where food skilfully prepared is calculated to satisfy the most discerning palate. Luncheons and dinners are served seven days a week with traditional roasts on Sundays.

In peaceful, rolling countryside near the Cheshire/Staffordshire border, this is a tranquil place in which to stay and the hostelry has elegantly colour-co-ordinated guest rooms, all with spacious bathrooms, LCD colour television, direct-dial telephone and tea and coffee-making facilities amongst their impressive appointments. Wireless internet access available.

**e-mail: theploughinn@hotmail.co.uk
www.theploughinnateaton.co.uk**

Horse & Farrier Inn

Threlkeld • Keswick • Cumbria

For over 300 years The Horse & Farrier has enjoyed an idyllic location in the centre of the picturesque village of Threlkeld, just 4 miles east of Keswick. Situated beneath Blencathra, with stunning views looking over towards the Helvellyn Range, this traditional Lakeland Inn offers a warm Cumbrian welcome to all its customers.

Mellow Lakeland stone, traditional architecture and such a peaceful setting make the Horse & Farrier a perfect place to enjoy a quiet pint, delicious food or a short break "away from it all". With superb Lakeland walks on your doorstep including Blencathra and Skiddaw and the Cumbria Way, we're ideally situated for walkers.

Our Restaurant is well known locally for the quality and imagination of its food and our Bar serves some of the best Jennings real ales in the Lake District.

Together with our 9 well appointed en suite bed & breakfast rooms, this really is a special place to spend some time. Well behaved pets are welcome.

Horse & Farrier Inn, Threlkeld, Keswick, Cumbria CA12 4SQ
Tel: 017687 79688 • Fax: 017687 79823
info@horseandfarrier.com • www.horseandfarrier.com

enjoyEngland.com
★★★★
INN

Broughton-in-Furness, Windermere

Ashbourne

Kilburn

THE FORRESTERS ARMS HOTEL
Kilburn, North Yorkshire YO61 4AH

Dating from the 12th century, this is one of England's oldest inns. The Henry Dee Bar still retains evidence of the days when it was the stable and the cosy lower bar has an unusual rounded stone chimney breast where log fires exude cheer in chilly weather. Both bars are furnished with the work of Robert Thompson (the 'Mouseman') who carved a tiny mouse on every piece of furniture produced. Real ale is available in convivial surroundings and ample and well-presented Yorkshire fare will more than satisfy the healthiest appetite.

This is the heart of James Herriot Country, within the North York Moors National Park, and the hotel is well recommended as a touring base, having outstanding accommodation.

Tel: 01347 868386 • e-mail: admin@forrestersarms.com • www.forrestersarms.com

Alford

KILDRUMMY INN
Kildrummy, Alford AB33 8QS
enquiries@kildrummyinn.co.uk • www.kildrummyinn.co.uk

• Located in the heart of rural Aberdeenshire, along the main A97, an excellent base for touring. • All bedrooms are en suite, with tea/coffee making, radio alarm and TV. • Superior quality cuisine is available in the comfortable Dining Rooms or in the relaxed atmosphere of the Sun Lounge. • Separate guests' TV lounge. • Ample parking.

Tel: 01975 571227

Local places of interest & activities include: • Kildrummy Castle & Gardens • Huntly Castle • Golf Courses • Pony trekking • Cycling • Hillwalking • Museums • Outdoor pursuits

---

Accommodation available	**Wi-Fi**	Wi-Fi available
Food available		Pets welcome
P Parking		Children welcome

Craignure (Isle of Mull)

Craignure Inn
Craignure, Isle of Mull, Argyll, PA65 6AY

Craignure Inn is a small characteristic old drovers' inn providing excellent service, food and accommodation whether you're looking for a longer holiday, full of fun outdoor wildlife activities, or simply a relaxing short break for you and your family, partner or friend.

The main attractions of the island, Torosay Castle and its gardens, and Duart

Castle with its Clan Maclean history, are at your doorstep. If you are lucky you might just see dolphins in Craignure Bay and otters just across the road by the rocks on the seashore. The Inn is open all year and prides itself on its friendly staff and warm welcome. It is favoured by locals and visitors alike.

There are three letting rooms, all en suite, with colour television and tea/coffee making facilities. The bar has a wide range of malts, fine wines, a large fire for the cooler evenings, outdoor seating and a cosy lounge.

There is an extensive bar menu with many wholesome, home cooked offerings using local produce such as Highland Beef, Hebridean Lamb, Mussels, Mull Cheddar and Smoked Trout.

We have regular live entertainment and welcome well behaved dogs. We provide information on local walks, trips and tours. Bus tours leave from Craignure, making it a great base for those without their own transport.

Craignure Inn

Isle of Mull, Argyll PA65 6AY
Tel: 016808 12305
craignureinn@btconnect.com
www.craignure-inn.co.uk

Pet-Friendly Accommodation

A selection of self-catering properties where pets are welcome.

Please contact individual proprietors for full details

and whether there is any charge for pets.

Counties are arranged in A-Z order within each country.

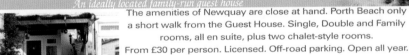

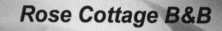

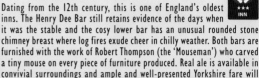

Visit the FHG website
www.holidayguides.com
for all kinds of holiday
accommodation in Britain

Please note...

INTERNET & Wi-Fi Access

All the properties below provide Internet or WiFi access for their visitors.

•CORNWALL

PORT ISAAC • *Self-catering*

The Garden House. Contact Mr D. Oldham, Trevella, Treveighan, Bodmin PL30 3JN
Tel: 01208 850529
e-mail: david.trevella@btconnect.com
website: www.trevellacornwall.co.uk

Wi-Fi internet access up to 4MB. Broadband powerline networking. Available in lounge/dining room. Free.

•CUMBRIA

CARLISLE • *Guest House*

Cornerways Guest House, 107 Warwick Road, Carlisle CA1 1EA
Tel: 01228 521733
e-mail: info@cornerwaysbandb.co.uk
website: www.cornerwaysbandb.co.uk

Wi Fi available in all bedrooms and public areas, free of charge. Broadband (high speed). Secure network.

KESWICK • *Self-catering Cottages*

Irton House Farm, Isel, Cockermouth CA13 9ST
Tel: 017687 76380
e-mail: joan@irtonhousefarm.co.uk
website: www.irtonhousefarm.com

Wi Fi available.

•DERBYSHIRE

ASHBOURNE • *Self-catering*

Paddock House Farm Holiday Cottages, Alstonefield, Ashbourne DE6 2FT
Tel: 01335 310282
e-mail: info@paddockhousefarm.co.uk
website: www.paddockhousefarm.co.uk

Wi Fi available.

•DORSET

BOURNEMOUTH • *Self-catering*

Bournemouth Holiday Apartments, 6 Forest Edge Drive, Bournemouth BH5 1HF
Tel: 01202 304925
e-mail: mikelyn-lambert@btinternet.com.
website: www.selfcateringbournemouth.co.uk

Wi-Fi access points on all floors throughout.

MIDDLEMARSH/SHERBORNE • *Self-catering*

White Horse Farm, Middle Marsh, Sherborne DT9 5QN
Tel: 01963 210222
e-mail: enquiries@whitehorsefarm.co.uk
website: www.whitehorsefarm.co.uk

Wi-Fi access in all properties.

•LINCOLNSHIRE

BARNOLDBY-LE-BECK • *Self-catering*

Grange Farm Holiday Cottages, Waltham Road, Barnoldby-le-Beck DN37 0AR
Tel: 01472 822216.
e-mail: sueuk4000@netscape-net
website: www.grangefarmcottages.com

Wi-Fi connection available in every room. £10 per stay.

•NORTHUMBERLAND

HEXHAM • *B&B*

Coach House B&B, South View/Tavern House, Bardon Mill, Hexham NE47 7HZ
Tel: 01434 344779
e-mail: mail@bardonmillcoachhouse.co.uk
website: www.bardonmillcoachhouse.co.uk

Free Wi-Fi available at breakfast time in the dining room; computer available for guests' use.

Please mention this FHG Guide when enquiring about accommodation featured in these pages

•OXFORDSHIRE

DIDCOT • *B&B*

Middle Fell B&B, Moreton Road, Aston Upthorpe, Didcot OX11 9ER
Tel: 01235 850207 or 07833 920678
e-mail: middlefell@ic24.net
website: www.middlefell.co.uk

Wi-Fi connection in every room free of charge.

•SOMERSET

BATH • *B&B*

Marlborough House, Marlborough Lane, Bath BA1 2NQ
Tel: 01225 318175
www.marlborough-house.net

Wi-Fi internet access available in all bedrooms, free of charge.

EXMOOR • *Self-catering*

West Hollowcombe Self-Catering Cottages, Hawkridge, Near Dulverton TA22 9QL
Tel: 01398 341 400
e-mail: info@westhollowcombe.co.uk
website: www.westhollowcombe.co.uk.

Internet access via BT Broadband Open Zone. Normally available within each cottage, but depends on atmospheric conditions. A separate room for communal use provides guaranteed availability at no charge.

NORTH PERROTT • *Self-catering*

Wood Dairy, Wood Lane, North Perrott TA18 7TA   Tel: 01935 891532
e-mail: liz@acountryretreat.co.uk
website: www.acountryretreat.co.uk

Wi-Fi connection at no charge (please bring own laptop).

•EAST SUSSEX

RYE • *Hotel*

Rye Lodge Hotel, Hilders Cliff, Rye TN31 7LD
Tel: 01797 223838
e-mail: info@ryelodge.co.uk
website: www.ryelodge.co.uk

Wi-Fi available in all rooms free of charge.

•NORTH YORKSHIRE

SKIPTON • *Self-catering*

Holiday Cottages (Yorkshire) Ltd, Water Street, Skipton BD23 1PB Tel: 01756 700510
e-mail: info@holidaycotts.co.uk.
website: www.holidaycotts.co.uk

Several cottages have Wi-Fi connection (search facility on website). Mostly free, but some may charge extra.

HELMSLEY • *Self-catering*

Valley View Farm, Old Byland, Helmsley, York YO62 5LG
Tel: 01439 798221
e-mail: sally@valleyviewfarm.com
website: www.valleyviewfarm.com

Wi-Fi connection in all cottages, free of charge.

•ARGYLL & BUTE

ISLE OF SEIL • *Self-catering*

Kilbride Croft, Balvicar, Isle of Seil PA34 4RD
Tel: 01852 300475.
e-mail: kilbridecroft@aol.com
website: www.kilbridecroft.co.uk

Wi-Fi available in Croft Cottage.

•HIGHLANDS

KINCRAIG • *Self-catering*

Alvie Holiday Cottages, Kincraig, Kingussie PH21 1NE
Tel: 01540 651255.
e-mail: info@alvie-estate.co.uk.
website: www.alvie-estate.co.uk.

BT Wi-Fi router in holiday properties. Free of charge.

•PERTH & KINROSS

PERTH • *Self-catering*

Cloag Farm Cottages, Methven, Perth PH1 3RR
Tel: 01738 840239
e-mail: info@cloagfarm.co.uk
website: www.cloagfarm.co.uk

Wireless broadband available.

Visit the FHG website www.holidayguides.com
for details of the wide choice of accommodation
featured in the full range of FHG titles

DIRECTORY OF WEBSITE AND E-MAIL ADDRESSES

A quick-reference guide to holiday accommodation with an e-mail address and/or website, conveniently arranged by country and county, with full contact details.

•LONDON

Hotel
Athena Hotel, 110-114 Sussex Gardens,
Hyde Park, LONDON W2 1UA
Tel: 020 7706 3866
• e-mail: stay@athenahotellondon.co.uk
• website: www.athenahotel.co.uk

B & B
Hanwell B & B, 110a Grove Avenue,
Hanwell, LONDON W7 3ES
Tel: 020 8567 5015
• e-mail: tassanimation@aol.com
• website: www.ealing-hanwell-bed-and-breakfast.co.uk/new/index

Hotel
Queens Hotel, 33 Anson Road,
Tufnell Park, LONDON N7 0RB
Tel: 020 7607 4725
• e-mail:stay@queenshotellondon.co.uk
• website: www.queenshotellondon.co.uk

•BERKSHIRE

Touring Campsite
Wellington Country Park, Odiham Road,
Riseley, Near READING, Berkshire
RG7 1SP
Tel : 0118 932 6444
• e-mail: info@wellington-country-park.co.uk
• website: www.wellington-country-park.co.uk

•CAMBRIDGESHIRE

Guest House
Hamden Guest House, 89 High Street,
Cherry Hinton, CAMBRIDGE,
Cambridgeshire CB1 9LU
Tel: 01223 413263
• e-mail: info@hamdenguesthouse.co.uk
• website: www.hamdenguesthouse.co.uk

•CHESHIRE

Farmhouse B & B
Astle Farm East, Chelford,
MACCLESFIELD, Cheshire SK10 4TA
Tel: 01625 861270
• e-mail: stubg@aol.com
• website: www.astlefarmeast.co.uk

•CORNWALL

Self-Catering
Penrose Burden Holiday Cottages,
St Breward, BODMIN, Cornwall
PL30 4LZ
Tel : 01208 850277
• website: www.penroseburden.co.uk

Self-Catering
Mr P. Watson, Creekside Holiday Houses,
Restronguet, FALMOUTH,
Cornwall TR11 5ST
Tel: 01326 372722
• website: www.creeksideholidayhouses.co.uk

Self-Catering
Fowey Harbour Cottages c/o WJB Hill &
Son, 3 Fore Street, FOWEY,
Cornwall PL23 1AH
Tel: 01726 832211
• e-mail: hillandson@talk21.com
• website: www.foweyharbourcottages.co.uk

Self-Catering / Caravan
Mrs A. E. Moore, Hollyvagg Farm,
Lewannick, LAUNCESTON,
Cornwall PL15 7QH
Tel: 01566 782309
• website: www.hollyvaggfarm.co.uk

Self-Catering
Butterdon Mill Holiday Homes,
Merrymeet, LISKEARD, Cornwall
PL14 3LS
Tel: 01579 342636
• e-mail: butterdonmillst@btconnect.com
• website: www.bmhh.co.uk

Self-Catering
Celia Hutchinson, Caradon Country
Cottages, East Taphouse, LISKEARD,
Cornwall PL14 4NH
Tel: 01579 320355
• e-mail: celia@caradoncottages.co.uk
• website: www.caradoncottages.co.uk

Self- Catering
Mr Lowman, Cutkive Wood Holiday Lodges,
St Ive, LISKEARD, Cornwall PL14 3ND
Tel: 01579 362216
• e-mail: holidays@cutkivewood.co.uk
• website: www.cutkivewood.co.uk

Self-Catering
Valleybrook Holidays, Peakswater, Lansallos,
LOOE, Cornwall PL13 2QE
Tel: 01503 220493
• e-mail: admin@valleybrookholidays.com
• website: www.valleybrookholidays.com

Guest House
Mrs Dewolfreys, Dewolf Guest House, 100
Henver Road, NEWQUAY, Cornwall TR7 3BL
Tel: 01637 874746
• e-mail: holidays@dewolfguesthouse.com
• website: www.dewolfguesthouse.com

Caravan / Camping
Quarryfield Caravan & Camping Park,
Crantock, NEWQUAY, Cornwall
Contact: Mrs A Winn, Tretherras, Newquay,
Cornwall TR7 2RE
Tel: 01637 872792
• e-mail:
quarryfield@crantockcaravans.orangehome.co.uk
• website: www.quarryfield.co.uk

B&B
Bolankan Cottage B & B, Crows-an-Wra,
St Buryan, PENZANCE, Cornwall TR19 6HU
Tel: 01736 810168
• e-mail: bolankancottage@talktalk.net
• website: www.bolankan-cottage.co.uk

Caravan / Camping
Globe Vale Holiday Park, Radnor, REDRUTH,
Cornwall TR16 4BH
Tel: 01209 891183
• e-mail: info@globevale.co.uk
• website: www.globevale.co.uk

Guest House
Mr S Hope, Dalswinton House,
ST MAWGAN-IN-PYDAR, Cornwall TR8 4EZ
Tel: 01637 860385
• e-mail: dalswintonhouse@btconnect.com
• website: www.dalswinton.com

Self-Catering
Maymear Cottage, ST TUDY
Contact: Ruth Reeves, Polstraul, Trewalder,
Delabole, Cornwall PL33 9ET
Tel: 01840 213120
• e-mail: ruth.reeves@hotmail.co.uk
• website: www.maymear.co.uk

Self-Catering
The Garden House, Port Isaac, Near
WADEBRIDGE, Cornwall
Contact: Mr D Oldham, Trevella,
Treveighan, St Teath, Cornwall PL30 3JN
Tel: 01208 850529
• e-mail: david.trevella@btconnect.com
• website: www.trevellacornwall.co.uk

•CUMBRIA

Guest House / Self- Catering
Cuckoo's Nest & Smallwood House,
Compston Road, AMBLESIDE, Cumbria
LA22 9DJ
Tel: 015394 32330
• e-mail: enq@cottagesambleside.co.uk
        enq@smallwoodhotel.co.uk
• website: www.cottagesambleside.co.uk
        www.smallwoodhotel.co.uk

Caravan Park
Greenhowe Caravan Park, Great Langdale,
AMBLESIDE, Cumbria LA22 9JU
Tel: 015394 37231
•website: www.greenhowe.com

Self-Catering
Lakelovers, Belmont House, Lake Road,
BOWNESS-ON-WINDERMERE LA23 3BJ
Tel: 015394 88855
• website: www.lakelovers.co.uk

Hotel
The Borrowdale Gates Hotel,
GRANGE-IN-BORROWDALE, Keswick,
Cumbria CA12 5UQ
Tel: 017687 77204
• e-mail: hotel@borrowdale-gates.com
• website: www.borrowdale-gates.com

Self-Catering
3 Randle Howe, Eskdale, HOLMROOK.
Contact: Susan Wedley, Long Hocking How,
Eskdale Green, Holmrook CA19 1UA
Tel: 01946 723126
• e-mail: jswedley@btinternet.com
• www.randlehow.co.uk

•• FHG GUIDES ••

Self-Catering
Mrs Almond, Irton House Farm, Isel, Near KESWICK, Cumbria CA13 9ST
Tel: 017687 76380
• e-mail: joan@irtonhousefarm.co.uk
• website: www.irtonhousefarm.com

Self-Catering
Mr D Williamson, Derwent Water Marina, Portinscale, KESWICK, Cumbria CA12 5RF
Tel: 017687 72912
• e-mail: info@derwentwatermarina.co.uk
• website: www.derwentwatermarina.co.uk

Inn
Horse and Farrier Inn, Threlkeld, KESWICK, Cumbria CA12 4SQ
Tel: 017687 79688
• e-mail: info@horseandfarrier.com
• website: www.horseandfarrier.com

Self-Catering
Mrs S.J. Bottom, Crossfield Cottages, KIRKOSWALD, Penrith, Cumbria CA10 1EU
Tel: 01768 898711
• e-mail: info@crossfieldcottages.co.uk
• website: www.crossfieldcottages.co.uk

•DERBYSHIRE

Self-Catering Holiday Cottages
Mark Redfern, Paddock House Farm Holiday Cottages, Peak District National Park, Alstonefield, ASHBOURNE, Derbyshire DE6 2FT
Tel: 01335 310282 / 07977 569618
• e-mail: info@paddockhousefarm.co.uk
• website: www.paddockhousefarm.co.uk

Caravan
Golden Valley Caravan Park, Coach Road, RIPLEY, Derbyshire DE55 4ES
Tel: 01773 513881
• e-mail: enquiries@goldenvalleycaravanpark.co.uk
• website: www.goldenvalleycaravanpark.co.uk

•DEVON

Hotel
Fairwater Head Hotel, Hawkchurch, Near AXMINSTER, Devon EX13 5TX
Tel: 01297 678349
• e-mail: info@fairwaterheadhotel.co.uk
• website: www.fairwaterheadhotel.co.uk

Farm B & B
Mrs J Ley, West Barton, Alverdiscott, Near BARNSTABLE, Devon EX31 3PT
Tel: 01271 858230
• e-mail: ela@andrews78.freeserve.co.uk

Self-Catering / B&B
Lake House Cottages and B&B, Lake Villa, BRADWORTHY, Devon EX22 7SQ
Tel : 01409 241962
• email: lesley@lakevilla.co.uk
• website: www.lakevilla.co.uk

Guest House
Woodlands Guest House, Parkham Road, BRIXHAM, South Devon TQ5 9BU
Tel: 01803 852040
• e-mail: woodlandsbrixham@btinternet.com
• website: www.woodlandsbrixham.co.uk

Self-Catering
Linda & Jim Watt, Northcote Manor Farm Holiday Cottages, Kentisbury, COMBE MARTIN, Devon EX31 4NB
Tel: 01271 882376
• e-mail: info@northcotemanorfarm.co.uk
• website: www.northcotemanorfarm.co.uk

Self-Catering
G Davidson Richmond, Clooneavin, Clooneavin Path, LYNMOUTH, Devon EX35 6EE
Tel: 01598 753334
• e-mail: relax@clooneavinholidays.co.uk
• website: www.clooneavinholidays.co.uk

B & B
Merritt House, 7 Queens Road, PAIGNTON, Devon TQ4 6AT
• e-mail: bookings@merritthouse.co.uk
• website: www.merritthouse.co.uk

Visit the FHG website
www.holidayguides.com
for all kinds of holiday accommodation in Britain

Guest House
A J Hill, Beaumont, Castle Hill, SEATON,
Devon EX12 2QW
Tel: 01297 20832
• e-mail: tony@lymebay.demon.co.uk
• website:
www.smoothhound.co.uk/hotels/beaumon1.html

Caravans / Camping
Salcombe Regis Camping & Caravan
Park, SIDMOUTH, Devon EX10 0JH
Tel: 01395 514303
• e-mail: contact@salcombe-regis.co.uk
• website: www.salcombe-regis.co.uk

Self-Catering / Camping
Dartmoor Country Holidays, Magpie Leisure
Park, Bedford Bridge, Horrabridge,
Yelverton, TAVISTOCK, Devon PL20 7RY
Tel: 01822 852651
• website: www.dartmoorcountryholidays.co.uk

Caravan / Camping Park
Harford Bridge Holiday Park, Peter Tavy,
TAVISTOCK, Devon PL19 9LS
Tel: 01822 810349
• email: enquiry@harfordbridge.co.uk
• website: www.harfordbridge.co.uk

Holiday Park
Langstone Manor Holiday Park,
Moortown, TAVISTOCK,
Devon PL19 9JZ
Tel: 01822 613371
• e-mail: web@langstonemanor.co.uk
• website: www.langstonemanor.co.uk

B&B
Sampford Manor, Sampford Spiney,
Yelverton, TAVISTOCK, Devon PL20 6LH
Tel: 01822 853442
• e-mail:
manor@sampford-spiney.fsnet.co.uk
• website:
www.sampford-spiney.fsnet.co.uk

Caravan & Camping
North Morte Farm Caravan & Camping Park,
Mortehoe, WOOLACOMBE, Devon EX34 7EG
Tel: 01271 870381
• e-mail: info@northmortefarm.co.uk
• website: www.northmortefarm.co.uk

Holiday Park
Woolacombe Bay Holiday Parks,
WOOLACOMBE, Devon
Tel: 0844 770 0384
• website: www.woolacombe.com

•DORSET

Self-Catering
Bournemouth Holiday Apartments, 15
Florence Road, BOURNEMOUTH, Dorset
BH5 1HF
Tel: 01202 304925
• e-mail: mikelyn_lambert@btinternet.com
• website: www.selfcateringbournemouth.co.uk

Guest House
Southbourne Grove Hotel, 96 Southbourne
Road, BOURNEMOUTH, Dorset BH6 3QQ
Tel: 01202 420503
• e-mail: neil@pack1462.freeserve.co.uk
• website: www.southbournegrovehotel.co.uk

Self-Catering
C. Hammond, Stourcliffe Court, 56
Stourcliffe Avenue, Southbourne,
BOURNEMOUTH, Dorset BH6 3PX
Tel: 01202 420698
• e-mail: rjhammond1@hotmail.co.uk
• website: www.stourcliffecourt.co.uk

Self-Catering Cottage / Farmhouse B & B
Mrs S. E. Norman, Frogmore Farm,
Chideock, BRIDPORT, Dorset DT6 6HT
Tel: 01308 456159
• e-mail: bookings@frogmorefarm.com
• website: www.frogmorefarm.com

B&B
Nethercroft, Winterbourne Abbas,
DORCHESTER, Dorset DT2 9LU
Tel: 01305 889337
• e-mail: val.bradbeer@btconnect.com
• website: www.nethercroft.com

Self-Catering
Josephine Pearse, Tamarisk Farm Cottages,
Beach Road, West Bexington,
DORCHESTER, Dorset DT2 9DF
Tel: 01308 897784
• e-mail: holidays@tamariskfarm.com
• website: www.tamariskfarm.com/holidays

Farmhouse B&B / Caravan & Camping
Luckford Wood Farmhouse, Church
Lane, East Stoke, Wareham, Near
LULWORTH, Dorset BH20 6AW
Tel: 01929 463098 / 07737 742615
• e-mail: luckfordleisure@hotmail.co.uk
• website: www.luckfordleisure.co.uk

Self-Catering
Westover Farm Cottages, Wootton Fitzpaine,
Near LYME REGIS, Dorset DT6 6NE
Tel: 01297 560451/561395
• e-mail: wfcottages@aol.com
• website: www.westoverfarmcottages.co.uk

Hotel
The Knoll House, STUDLAND BAY,
Dorset BH19 3AW
Tel: 01929 450450
• e-mail: info@knollhouse.co.uk
• website: www.knollhouse.co.uk

Hotel
Manor House Hotel, STUDLAND, Dorset
BH19 3AU
Tel: 01929 450288
• e-mail: info@themanorhousehotel.com
• website: www.themanorhousehotel.com

Inn B&B
The White Swan, The Square, 31 High
Street, SWANAGE BN19 2LJ
Tel: 01929 423804
• e-mail: info@whiteswanswanage.co.uk
• website: www.whiteswanswanage.co.uk

•GLOUCESTERSHIRE

Self-Catering
Two Springbank, 37 Hopton Road, Cam,
DURSLEY, Gloucs GL11 5PD
Contact: Mrs F A Jones, 32 Everlands, Cam,
Dursley, Gloucs G11 5NL
Tel: 01453 543047
• e-mail: info@twospringbank.co.uk
• website: www.twospringbank.co.uk

B & B
Mrs A Rhoton, Hyde Crest, Cirencester Road,
Minchinhampton, STROUD, Gloucs GL6 8PE
Tel: 01453 731631
• e-mail: stay@hydecrest.co.uk
• website: www.hydecrest.co.uk

•HAMPSHIRE

Holiday Park
Downton Holiday Park, Shorefield Road,
Milford-on-Sea, LYMINGTON, Hampshire
SO41 0LH
Tel: 01425 476131 / 01590 642515
• e-mail: info@downtonholidaypark.co.uk
• website: www.downtonholidaypark.co.uk

•KENT

Self-Catering
Cottage Farm Self-Catering
Accommodation, Cackets Lane, Cudham,
Near SEVENOAKS, Kent TN14 7QG
Tel: 01959 534048
• cottagefarmaccommodation@googlemail.com
• website: www.cottagefarmgardens.com

•LANCASHIRE

Guest House
Parr Hall Farm, Parr Lane, Eccleston,
Chorley, PRESTON, Lancs PR7 5SL
Tel: 01257 451917
• e-mail: enquiries@parrhallfarm.com
• website: www.parrhallfarm.com

•LINCOLNSHIRE

Self-Catering
Grange Farm Cottages, Waltham Road,
BARNOLDBY-LE-BECK, N.E. Lincolnshire
DN37 0AR
Tel: 01472 822216
• e-mail: sueuk4000@netscape.net
• website: www.grangefarmcottages.com

Self-catering
Paul & Flora Bennett, Brackenborough
Hall Coach House Holidays, LOUTH,
Lincolnshire LN11 0NS
Tel: 01507 603193
• e-mail:
paulandflora@brackenboroughhall.com
• website: www.brackenboroughhall.com

•NORFOLK

Holiday Park
Castaways Holiday Park, Paston Road,
BACTON-ON-SEA, Norfolk NR12 0JB
Tel : 01692 650436
• e-mail: info@castawaysholidaypark.net
• website: www.castawaysholidaypark.net

Self-catering
Scarning Dale, Dale Road, Scarning,
DEREHAM, Norfolk NR19 2QN
Tel: 01362 687269
• e-mail: jean@scarningdale.co.uk
• website: www.scarningdale.co.uk

Holiday Park
Waveney Valley Holiday Park, Airstation
Lane, Rushall, DISS, Norfolk IP21 4QF
Tel: 01379 741228
• e-mail: waveneyvalleyhp@aol.com
• website: www.caravanparksnorfolk.co.uk

Self-Catering
Blue Riband Holidays, HEMSBY,
Great Yarmouth, Norfolk NR29 4HA
Tel: 01493 730445
• website: www.BlueRibandHolidays.co.uk

Self-Catering
Winterton Valley Holidays, Edward Road,
WINTERTON-ON-SEA, Norfolk NR29 4BX
Contact:15 Kingston Avenue, Caister-on-
Sea, Norfolk NR30 5ET
Tel: 01493 377175
• e-mail: info@wintertonvalleyholidays.co.uk
• website: www.wintertonvalleyholidays.co.uk

•NORTHUMBERLAND

Self-Catering
Bank House Holiday Cottages,
GUYZANCE, Northumberland NE65 9AP
Tel: 07957 100615
• e-mail:
info@bankhouseholidaycottages.co.uk
• website:
www.bankhouseholidaycottages.co.uk

•NOTTINGHAMSHIRE

Caravan & Camping Park
Orchard Park, Marnham Road, Tuxford,
NEWARK, Nottinghamshire NG22 0PY
Tel: 01777 870228
• e-mail: info@orchardcaravanpark.co.uk
• website: www.orchardcaravanpark.co.uk

•OXFORDSHIRE

B&B
Middle Fell, Moreton Road, Aston Upthorpe,
DIDCOT, Oxfordshire OX11 9ER
Tel: 01235 850207
• e-mail: middlefell@ic24.net
• website: www.middlefell.co.uk

B & B / Guest House
June Collier, Colliers, 55 Nethercote Road,
Tackley, KIDLINGTON, Oxfordshire OX5 3AT
Tel: 01869 331255 / 07790 338225
• e-mail: junecollier@btinternet.com
• website: www.colliersbnb.co.uk

Guest House
The Bungalow, Cherwell Farm, Mill
Lane, Old Mawston, OXFORD OX3 0QF
Tel: 01865 557171
• e-mail: ros.bungalowbb@btinternet.com
• website:
www.cherwellfarm-oxford-accom.co.uk

•SHROPSHIRE

Hotel
Longmynd Hotel, Cunnery Rd, CHURCH
STRETTON, Shropshire SY6 6AG
Tel: 01694 722244
• e-mail: info@longmynd.co.uk
• website: www.longmynd.co.uk

Self-Catering
Clive & Cynthia Prior, Mocktree Barns
Holiday Cottages, Leintwardine, LUDLOW,
Shropshire SY7 0LY
Tel: 01547 540441
• e-mail: mocktreebarns@care4free.net
• website: www.mocktreeholidays.co.uk

Self-Catering
Jane Cronin, Sutton Court Farm Cottages,
Sutton Court Farm, Little Sutton, LUDLOW,
Shropshire SY8 2AJ
Tel: 01584 861305
• e-mail: enquiries@suttoncourtfarm.co.uk
• website: www.suttoncourtfarm.co.uk

•SOMERSET

Farm / Guest House / Self-Catering
Jackie Bishop, Toghill House Farm, Freezing
Hill, Wick, Near BATH, Somerset BS30 5RT
Tel: 01225 891261
• e-mail:
accommodation@toghillhousefarm.co.uk
• website: www.toghillhousefarm.co.uk

Self-Catering
Westward Rise Holiday Park, South Road,
BREAN, Burnham-on-Sea, Somerset TA8 2RD
Tel: 01278 751310
• e-mail: info@westwardrise.com
• website: www.westwardrise.com

Self-Catering / Holiday Park / Touring Pitches
Mary Randle, St Audries Bay Holiday Club,
West Quantoxhead, MINEHEAD, Somerset
TA4 4DY
Tel: 01984 632515
• e-mail: info@staudriesbay.co.uk
• website: www.staudriesbay.co.uk

B & B
The Old Mill, Netherclay, Bishop's Hull,
TAUNTON, Somerset TA1 5AB
Tel: 01823 289732
• website: www.theoldmillbandb.co.uk /
www.bandbtaunton.co.uk

FHG Guides publish a large range of well-known accommodation guides. We will be happy to send you details or you can use the order form in this book.

Farm / Guest House
G. Clark, Yew Tree Farm, THEALE,
Near Wedmore, Somerset BS28 4SN
Tel: 01934 712475
• e-mail: enquiries@yewtreefarmbandb.co.uk
• website: www.yewtreefarmbandb.co.uk

B & B
Mrs S Crane, Birdwood House, Bath Road,
WELLS, Somerset BA5 3EW
Tel: 01749 679250
• e-mail: info@birdwood-bandb.co.uk
• website: www.birdwood-bandb.co.uk

• STAFFORDSHIRE

Self-Catering
T.A. Mycock, Rosewood Cottage, Lower
Berkhamsytch, Bottom House, Near LEEK,
Staffordshire ST13 7QP
Tel: 01538 308213
• website: www.rosewoodcottage.co.uk

• SUFFOLK

Self-Catering
Kessingland Cottages, Rider Haggard Lane,
KESSINGLAND, Suffolk.
Contact: S. Mahmood, 156 Bromley Road,
Beckenham, Kent BR3 6PG
Tel: 020 8650 0539
• e-mail: jeeptrek@kjti.co.uk
• website: www.k-cottage.co.uk

Holiday Park
Broadland Holiday Village, Oulton
Broad, LOWESTOFT, Suffolk NR33 9JY
Tel: 01502 573033
• e-mail: info@broadlandvillage.co.uk
• website: www.broadlandvillage.co.uk

• EAST SUSSEX

Hotel
Grand Hotel, 1 Grand Parade, St Leonards,
HASTINGS, East Sussex TN37 6AQ
Tel: 01424 428510
• e-mail: info@grandhotelhastings.co.uk
• website: www.grandhotelhastings.co.uk

Self-Catering
"Pekes", CHIDDINGLY, East Sussex
Contact: Eva Morris, 124 Elm Park
Mansions, Park Walk, London SW10 0AR
Tel: 020 7352 8088
• e-mail: pekes.afa@virgin.net
• website: www.pekesmanor.com

Guest House / Self-Catering
Longleys Farm Cottage, Harebeating Lane,
HAILSHAM, East Sussex BN27 1ER
Tel: 01323 841227
• website: www.longleysfarmcottage.co.uk

• WEST SUSSEX

Guest Accommodation
St Andrews Lodge, Chichester Road,
SELSEY, West Sussex PO20 0LX
Tel: 01243 606899
• e-mail: info@standrewslodge.co.uk
• website: www.standrewslodge.co.uk

• WARWICKSHIRE

Guest House
John & Julia Downie, Holly Tree
Cottage, Pathlow, STRATFORD-UPON-
AVON, Warwickshire CV37 0ES
Tel: 01789 204461
• e-mail: john@hollytree-cottage.co.uk
• website: www.hollytree-cottage.co.uk

• NORTH YORKSHIRE

Self-Catering
Rudding Holiday Park, Follifoot,
HARROGATE, North Yorkshire HG3 1JH
Tel: 01423 870439
• e-mail: stay@ruddingpark.com
• website: www.ruddingholidaypark.co.uk

Self-Catering
Southfield Farm Holiday Cottages,
Darley, HARROGATE, North Yorkshire
HG3 2PR
Tel: 01423 780258
• e-mail: info@southfieldcottages.co.uk
• website: www.southfieldcottages.co.uk

Farmhouse B & B
Mrs Julie Clarke, Middle Farm, Woodale,
Coverdale, LEYBURN, North Yorkshire
DL8 4TY • Tel: 01969 640271
• e-mail: j-a-clarke@hotmail.co.uk
• www.yorkshirenet.co.uk/stayat/middlefarm/
index.htm

Self-Catering
East Farm Country Cottages, SCALBY
NABS, Scarborough, N.Yorkshire
YO13 0SL
Tel: 01723 353635
• e-mail: joeastfarmcottages@hotmail.co.uk
• www.eastfarmcountrycottages.co.uk

Guest House / Self-Catering
Sue & Tony Hewitt, Harmony Country Lodge,
80 Limestone Road, Burniston,
SCARBOROUGH, North Yorkshire YO13 0DG
Tel: 01723 870276
• e-mail: mail@harmonylodge.net
• website: www.harmonycountrylodge.co.uk

Self-Catering
2 Hollies Cottages, Stainforth, SETTLE,
N.Yorkshire
Contact : Bridge Cottage, Stainforth,
Near Settle BD24 9PG
Tel: 01729 822649
• e-mail: vivmills30@hotmail.com
• website: www.stainforth-holiday-cottage-
settle.co.uk

B & B
Beck Hall, Cove Road, Malham,
SKIPTON, N.Yorkshire BD23 4DL
Tel: 01729 830332
• e-mail: alice@beckhallmalham.com
• website: www.beckhallmalham.com

Hotel
The Coniston Hotel, Coniston Cold,
SKIPTON, North Yorkshire BD23 4EA
Tel: 01756 748080
• e-mail: info@theconistonhotel.com
• website: www.theconistonhotel.com

Self-Catering
York Lakeside Lodges Ltd, Moor Lane,
YORK, North Yorkshire YO24 2QU
Tel: 01904 702346
• e-mail: neil@yorklakesidelodges.co.uk
• website: www.yorklakesidelodges.co.uk

WALES

•ANGLESEY & GWYNEDD

Self-Catering
Crugeran Farm Holidays, ABERSOCH
Contact : Mrs R Parry, Crugeran, Sarn
Mellteyrn, Pwllheli, Gwynedd LL53 8DT
Tel: 01758 730375
• e-mail: post@crugeran.com
• website: www.crugeran.com

Self-Catering / Caravan & Camping Park
Bryn Gloch Caravan and Camping Park,
Betws Garmon, CAERNARFON, Gwynedd
LL54 7YY Tel: 01286 650216
• e-mail: eurig@bryngloch.co.uk
• website: www.campwales.co.uk

Self-Catering Chalet
Chalet at Glan Gwna Holiday Park, Caethro,
CAERNARFON, Gwynedd
Contact: Mr H A Jones, Menai Bridge,
Caernarfon, Gwynedd LL59 5LN
Tel: 01248 712045
• e-mail: hajones@northwales-chalet.co.uk
• website: www.northwales-chalet.co.uk

Motel
The Beach Motel, Lon St Ffraid,
Trearddur Bay, HOLYHEAD, Anglesey
LL65 2YT
• e-mail: info@thebeachmotel.co.uk
• website: www.thebeachmotel.co.uk

Guest House
Cefn Uchaf Farm Guesthouse,
Garndolbenmaen, PORTHMADOG
LL51 9PJ Tel: 01766 530239
• e-mail: enquiries@cefnuchaf.co.uk
• website: www.cefnuchaf.com

Self-Catering
Parc Wernol, Chwilog Fawr, Chwilog,
PWLLHELI, Criccieth, Gwynedd LL53 6SW
Tel: 01766 810506
• e-mail: catherine@wernol.co.uk
• website: www.wernol.co.uk

•NORTH WALES

Self-Catering
Bron-Y-Wendon & Nant-Y-Glyn Holiday
Parks, Wern Road,Llanddulas, COLWYN
BAY, North Wales LL22 8HG
Tel: 01492 512903/512282
• e-mail: stay@northwales-holidays.co.uk
• website: www.northwales-holidays.co.uk

• PEMBROKESHIRE

Self-Catering
Llanteglos Estate, Llanteg, Near
AMROTH, Pembs SA67 8PU
• e-mail: llanteglosestate@supanet.com
• website: www.llanteglos-estate.com

Self-Catering
Timberhill Farm, BROAD HAVEN,
Pembrokeshire SA62 3LZ
Contact: Mrs L Ashton, 10 St Leonards
Road, Thames Ditton, Surrey KT7 0RJ
Tel: 02083 986349
• e-mail: lejash@aol.com
• website: www.33timberhill.com

Self-Catering
Quality Cottages, Cerbid, Solva,
HAVERFORDWEST, Pembrokeshire SA62 6YE
Tel: 01348 837871
• e-mail: reserve@qualitycottages.co.uk
• website: www.qualitycottages.co.uk

Golf Club / Resort
Newport Links Golf Club & Resort,
NEWPORT, Pembrokeshire SA42 0NR
Tel: 012239 820244
• e-mail: newportgc@lineone.net
• website: www.newportlinks.co.uk

Self-Catering
Ffynnon Ddofn, Llanon, Llanrhian, Near ST
DAVIDS, Pembrokeshire.
Contact: Mrs B. Rees White, Brick House
Farm, Burnham Road, Woodham Mortimer,
Maldon, Essex CM9 6SR. Tel: 01245 224611
• e-mail: daisypops@madasafish.com
• website: www.ffynnonddofn.co.uk

• POWYS

Self-Catering
Old Stables Cottage & Old Dairy, Lane Farm,
Paincastle, Builth Wells, HAY-ON-WYE,
Powys LD2 3JS
Tel: 01497 851 605
• e-mail: lanefarm@onetel.com
• website: www.lane-farm.co.uk

• SOUTH WALES

Campsite
Mr G. Watkins, Wernddu Caravan Park, Old
Ross Road, ABERGAVENNY,
Monmouthshire NP7 8NG
Tel:01873 856223
• e-mail: info@wernddu-golf-club.co.uk
• website: www.wernddu-golf-club.co.uk

SCOTLAND

•ANGUS & DUNDEE

Golf Club
Edzell Golf Club, High Street, EDZELL,
Brechin, Angus DD9 7TF
Tel: 01356 648462
• e-mail: secretary@edzellgolfclub.com
• website: www.edzellgolfclub.com

•ARGYLL & BUTE

Self-Catering
Appin House Lodges, APPIN, Argyll
PA38 4BN
Tel: 01631 730207
• e-mail: denys@appinhouse.co.uk
• website: www.appinhouse.co.uk

Self-Catering
Blarghour Farm Cottages, Blarghour Farm,
By Dalmally, INVERARAY, Argyll PA33 1BW
Tel: 01866 833246
• e-mail: blarghour@btconnect.com
• website: www.self-catering-argyll.co.uk

Self-Catering
Prospect House S/C Apartments & House,
ROTHESAY
Contact: Mrs A. Shaw, 21 Battery Place,
Rothesay, Isle of Bute PA20 9DU
Tel: 01700 503526
• e-mail: janmckirdy@aol.com
• website: www.prospecthouse-bute.co.uk

Hotel
Falls of Lora Hotel, Connel Ferry, By OBAN,
Argyll PA37 1PB
Tel: 01631 710483
• e-mail: enquiries@fallsoflora.com
• website: www.fallsoflora.com

•BORDERS

B & B
Hundalee House, JEDBURGH,
Roxburghshire TD8 6PA
Tel: 01835 863011
• e-mail: sheila.whittaker@btinternet.com
www.accommodation-scotland.org

B & B
The Garden House, Whitmuir, SELKIRK,
Borders TD7 4PZ
Tel: 01750 721728
• e-mail: whitmuir@btconnect.com
• website: www.whitmuirfarm.co.uk

•DUMFRIES & GALLOWAY

Self-Catering
Barend Holiday Village, Barend Farmhouse,
SANDYHILLS, Dalbeattie, Dumfries &
Galloway DG5 4NU
Tel: 01387 780663
•e-mail: info@barendholidayvillage.co.uk
•website: www.barendholidayvillage.co.uk

Self-Catering
Ae Farm Cottages, Gubhill Farm, Ae,
DUMFRIES, Dumfriesshire DG1 1RL
Tel: 01387 860648
•e-mail: gill@gubhill.co.uk
•website: www.aefarmcottages.co.uk

Self-Catering
Rusko Holidays, GATEHOUSE OF FLEET,
Castle Douglas, Dumfriesshire DG7 2BS
Tel: 01557 814215
• e-mail: info@ruskoholidays.co.uk
• website: www.ruskoholidays.co.uk

Hotel
Corsewall Lighthouse Hotel, Kirkcolm,
STRANRAER, Dumfries & Galloway
DG9 0QG Tel: 01776 853220
• e-mail info@lighthousehotel.co.uk
• website: www.lighthousehotel.co.uk

•EDINBURGH & LOTHIANS

Self-Catering
Mrs C. M. Kilpatrick, Slipperfield House,
WEST LINTON, Peeblesshire EH46 7AA
Tel: 01968 660401
• e-mail: cottages@slipperfield.com
• website: www.slipperfield.com

•FIFE

Guest House
The Spindrift Guest House, Pittenweem
Road, ANSTRUTHER, Fife KY10 3DT
Tel: 01333 310573
• e-mail: info@thespindrift.co.uk
• website: www.thespindrift.co.uk

•HIGHLANDS

Self-Catering
Frank & Juliet Spencer-Nairn, Culligran
Cottages, Struy, Near BEAULY, Inverness-
shire IV4 7JX . Tel: 01463 761285
• e-mail: info@culligrancottages.co.uk
• website: www.culligrancottages.co.uk

Hotel
The Clan MacDuff Hotel, Achintore Road,
FORT WILLIAM, Inverness-shire PH33 6RW
Tel: 01397 702341
• e-mail: reception@clanmacduff.co.uk
• website: www.clanmacduff.co.uk

Caravan Park
A.J.Davis, Gruinard Bay Caravan Park,
LAIDE, Ross-shire IV22 2ND
Tel: 01445 731225
• e-mail: gruinard@ecosse.net
• website: www.gruinard.scotshost.co.uk

Hotel
Whitebridge Hotel, Whitebridge, LOCH
NESS, Inverness-shire IV2 6UN
Tel: 01456 486226
• e-mail: info@whitebridgehotel.co.uk
• website: www.whitebridgehotel.co.uk

B & B / Self-Catering
Mondhuie Chalets & B&B, NETHY
BRIDGE, Inverness-shire PH25 3DF
Tel: 01479 821062
• e-mail: david@mondhuie.com
• website: www.mondhuie.com

B & B
Bruach Ard, POOLEWE
Tel: 01445 781765
• e-mail: dgeorge@globalnet.co.uk
• website: www.davidgeorge.co.uk

Self Catering
Broomview & Sunset Cottages, Rhiroy,
Lochbroom, By Garve, ULLAPOOL IV23 2QR
Contact: Mrs L Renwick, Spindrift, Keppoch
Farm, Dundonnell, Ross-shire IV23 2QR
Tel: 01854 633269
• e-mail: linda@lochbroomcottages.co.uk
• website: www.lochbroomcottages.co.uk

•LANARKSHIRE

Self-Catering
Carmichael Country Cottages, By BIGGAR,
Lanarkshire ML12 6PG
Tel: 01899 308336
• e-mail: information@carmichael.co.uk
• website: www.carmichael.co.uk

•PERTH & KINROSS

Self-Catering
Laighwood Holidays, Laighwood,
DUNKELD, Perthshire PH8 0HB
Tel: 01350 724241
• e-mail: holidays@laighwood.co.uk
• website: www.laighwood.co.uk

Self-Catering
Atholl Cottage, Killiecrankie, PITLOCHRY,
Perthshire PH16 5LR
Contact: Mrs Joan Troup, Dalnasgadh,
Killiecrankie, Pitlochry, Perthshire PH16 5LN
Tel: 01796 470017
• e-mail: info@athollcottage.co.uk
• website: www.athollcottage.co.uk

•ORKNEY

Caravan & Camping
Point of Ness, STROMNESS, Orkney
Tel: 01856 873535
• e-mail: recreation@orkney.gov.uk
• website: www.orkney.gov.uk

NORTHERN IRELAND

Caravan Park
Six Mile Water Carvan Park, Lough
Road, ANTRIM BT41 4DG
Tel: 028 9446 4963
• e-mail: sixmilewater@antrim.gov.uk
• website: www.antrim.gov.uk/caravanpark

**Please mention this
FHG Guide when enquiring about
accommodation
featured in these pages**

© FHG Guides Ltd, 2012
ISBN 978-1-85055-445-5

Typeset by FHG Guides Ltd, Paisley.
Printed and bound in China by Imago.

Distribution. Book Trade: ORCA Book Services, Stanley House,
3 Fleets Lane, Poole, Dorset BH15 3AJ
(Tel: 01202 665432; Fax: 01202 666219)
e-mail: mail@orcabookservices.co.uk
Published by FHG Guides Ltd., Abbey Mill Business Centre,
Seedhill, Paisley PA1 ITJ (Tel: 0141-887 0428 Fax: 0141-889 7204).
e-mail: admin@fhguides.co.uk

750 Bed & Breakfasts in Britain is published by FHG Guides Ltd,
part of Kuperard Group.

Cover design: FHG Guides
Cover Picture: with thanks to
The Woodside, Southbourne, Bournemouth, Dorset BH6 3SR (page 63)
York House, Heworth Green, York YO31 7TQ (page 216)